STATISTICS

Middles, Means, and In-Betweens

A unit of study for grades 5–6
from USED NUMBERS: REAL DATA IN THE CLASSROOM

Developed at Technical Education Research Centers and Lesley College

Susan N. Friel, Janice R. Mokros, and Susan Jo Russell

DALE SEYMOUR PUBLICATIONS

The *Used Numbers* materials were prepared with the support of National Science Foundation Grant No. MDR-8651649. Any opinions, findings, conclusions, or recommendations expressed in this publication are those of the authors and do not necessarily represent the views of the National Science Foundation. These materials shall be subject to a royalty-free, irrevocable, worldwide, nonexclusive license in the United States Government to reproduce, perform, translate, and otherwise use and to authorize others to use such materials for Government purposes.

Cover design and illustrations: Rachel Gage

Order number DS01039
ISBN 0-86651-518-6

DALE
SEYMOUR
PUBLICATIONS
P.O. BOX 10888
PALO ALTO. CA 94303

2 3 4 5 6 7 8 9 10-MA-96 95 94 93 92 91

USED NUMBERS STAFF

Co-principal investigators

Susan Jo Russell
Technical Education Research Centers (TERC)

Susan N. Friel
Lesley College

Curriculum development

Rebecca B. Corwin (TERC and Lesley College)
Tim Barclay (TERC)
Antonia Stone (Playing to Win)

Research and evaluation

Janice R. Mokros (TERC)
Alana Parkes (TERC)
Debra Gustafson (TERC)
Amy Weinberg (TERC)
John Olive (University of Georgia)
Deborah Ruff (University of Georgia)
Heide Wiegel (University of Georgia)
Bonnie Brownstein (Institute for Schools of the Future)
Ellen Bialo (Institute for Schools of the Future)
Michele Arsenault (Institute for Schools of the Future)
Mary Fullmer (University of Chicago)

Design and production

Elisabeth Roberts (TERC)
LeAnn Davis (TERC)
Jessica Goldberg (TERC)
John Abbe (TERC)
Edith Alvarenga (TERC)
Laurie Aragon (COMAP)

Cooperating classrooms for this unit

Barbara Bené
Newton Public Schools, Massachusetts

Lydia Polonsky
University of Chicago Lab School, Illinois

Daniel Klemmer
Cambridge Public Schools, Massachusetts

Nick Haddad
Fayerweather Street School, Cambridge, Massachusetts

Betsy Abernathy
Cambridge Friends School, Massachusetts

Advisory board

Joan Akers, California State Department of Education
Bonnie Brownstein, Institute for Schools of the Future
James Landwehr, AT&T Bell Laboratories
Steven Leinwand, Connecticut State Department of Education
John Olive, University of Georgia
David Pillemer, Wellesley College
Andee Rubin, Bolt Beranek and Newman Laboratories
Cindy Stephens, D. C. Heath
Marion Walter, University of Oregon
Virginia Wooley, Boston Museum of Science

Thanks also to advice and comment from Marilyn Burns, Solomon A. Garfunkel (COMAP), and Bob Willcutt.

For *Middles, Means, and In-Betweens*, the authors' names are listed alphabetically on the cover and title page.

CONTENTS

PREFACE

In an information-rich society such as ours, statistics are an increasingly important aspect of daily life. We are constantly bombarded with information about everything around us. This wealth of data can become confusing, or it can help us make choices about our actions.

Educators and mathematicians now stress the importance of incorporating data analysis and statistics into the elementary mathematics curriculum to prepare students for living and working in a world filled with information based on data. The *Curriculum and Evaluation Standards for School Mathematics*, published by the National Council of Teachers of Mathematics in 1989, highlights statistics as one of the key content strands for all grade levels.

Many teachers see the need to support students in becoming better problem solvers in mathematics. However, it is difficult to find problems that give students the kind of experiences they need, are manageable in the classroom, and lead to the learning of essential mathematics. The area of data analysis—collecting, organizing, graphing, and interpreting data—provides a feasible, engaging context in which elementary grade students can do real mathematics. Students of all ages are interested in real data about themselves and the world around them.

Teaching statistics: Pedagogical issues

We introduce students to good literature in their early years. We do not reserve great literature until they are older—on the contrary, we encourage them to read it or we read it to them. Similarly, we can give young students experience with real mathematical processes rather than save the good mathematics for later.

Through collecting and analyzing real data, students encounter the uncertainty and intrigue of real mathematics. Mathematicians do not sit at desks doing isolated problems. Instead, they discuss, debate, and argue—building theories and collecting data to support them, working cooperatively (and sometimes competitively) to refine and develop such theories further.

Mathematicians and scientists use information or data like snapshots to look at, describe, and better understand the world. They cope with the real-world "messiness" of the data they encounter, which often do not lead to a single, clear answer.

Because statistics is an application of real mathematics skills, it provides the opportunity to model real mathematical behaviors. As students engage in the study of statistics, they, like scientists and statisticians, participate in:

▼ cooperative learning

▼ theory building

▼ discussing and defining terms and procedures

▼ working with messy data

▼ dealing with uncertainty

We want elementary school students to have the opportunity to engage in such real mathematical behavior, discussing, describing, challenging each other, and building theories about real-world phenomena based on their work.

Data analysis in the mathematics curriculum

Exploring data involves students directly in many aspects of mathematics. Data are collected through counting and measuring; they are sorted and classified; they are represented through graphs, pictures, tables, and charts. In summarizing and comparing data, students calculate, estimate, and choose appropriate units. In the primary grades, work with data is closely tied to the number relationships and measuring processes that students are learning. In the upper elementary grades, students encounter some of the approaches used in statistics for describing data and making inferences. Throughout the data analysis process, students make decisions about how to count and measure, what degree of accuracy is appropriate, and how much information is enough; they continually make connections between the numbers and what those numbers represent.

Instead of doing mathematics as an isolated set of skills unrelated to the world of reality, students can understand statistics as the vibrant study of the world in which they live, where numbers can tell them many different stories about aspects of their own lives. The computation they do is for a purpose, and the analysis they do helps them to understand how mathematics can function as a significant tool in describing, comparing, predicting, and making decisions. ■

TEACHING DATA ANALYSIS

The nature of data analysis

In data analysis, students use numbers to describe, compare, predict, and make decisions. When they analyze data, they search for patterns and attempt to understand what those patterns tell them about the phenomena the data represent.

A data analysis investigation generally includes recognizable phases:

▼ considering the problem

▼ collecting and recording data

▼ representing the data

▼ describing and interpreting the data

▼ developing hypotheses and theories based on the data

These phases often occur in a cycle: the development of a theory based on the data often leads to a new question, which may begin the data analysis cycle all over again.

Elementary students can collect, represent, and interpret real data. Although their work differs in many ways from that of adult statisticians, their processes are very similar. Elementary school students can both analyze data and use those data to describe and make decisions about real situations.

Because real data are the basis for investigations in data analysis, there are no predetermined "answers." For example, if your class collects data on the ages of the students' siblings, the students understand that their job is more than simply coming up with an answer that you knew all along. Not only do you *not* know the answer in advance, but, without seeing the data, you may not even know what the most interesting questions are going to be!

While this situation encourages students to do their own mathematical thinking, it can also feel risky for you. Many teachers welcome a little uncertainty in their mathematics classes, when it prods their students to be more independent thinkers. To support you, the authors provide sample experiences from teachers who have used the activities described here so that you can be prepared for the kinds of issues that are likely to arise. You will soon build your own repertoire of experiences with data analysis activities and will be able to anticipate likely questions, confusions, and opportunities.

The importance of discussion in mathematics

A central activity in data analysis is dialogue and discussion. While it is easy for you and your students to become engaged and enthusiastic in collecting data and making graphs, a significant amount of time should also be devoted to reflection about the meaning of the data.

Since students are not used to talking much during their mathematics work, it is important to support active decisionmaking by the students from the very beginning of the investigation. Students' participation in framing the initial question, choosing the methods of investigation, and deciding on ways to organize their data is essential. Once the data are collected and organized, the students must grapple with interpreting the results. If you have the outcome of a discussion or the "teaching points" you want to make too clearly in mind, you may guide students' observations too quickly into predetermined channels. When student ideas are ignored, misinterpreted, or rejected, they soon understand that their job is to second-guess the "answer" you had in mind.

On the other hand, if students find that *anything* they say is accepted in the same way, if every contribution is "a good idea" and no idea is ever challenged, they can lose motivation to participate. Ask students to reflect on, clarify, and extend their ideas and to listen to and ask questions of each other. Discussions in mathematics should encourage students to interpret numbers, make conjectures, develop theories, consider opposing views, and support their ideas with reasons.

Sensitive issues in data analysis

Students of all ages are interested in data about themselves and the issues they care about. Topics that matter enough to students to make them compelling topics for study often have very personal aspects. Investigations about families, heights, or students' chores, for example, can all bring up sensitive issues. After trying many topics in many classrooms, we have concluded that the potential sensitivity of a topic is not a reason to avoid it; on the contrary, these are the very topics that most engage student interest. All teachers deal with difficult or sensitive issues in their classroom, and the skills demanded of a teacher in handling issues that arise during data analysis activities are no different. Keep in mind that students may

sometimes want their data to be anonymous. Focusing on the patterns and shape of the class data, rather than on individual pieces of data, is particularly helpful, especially for upper elementary students.

Small-group work

Many of the investigations involve students working in teams. At first, keep small-group sessions short and focused. For students not used to working in small groups, assign specific tasks that encourage the participation of all the group members. For example, instead of, "Have a discussion in your group to decide what you want to ask the second graders about their bedtimes," you might say, "Come up with three possible questions you could ask the second graders."

The small-group activities provide an opportunity for your students to work in a cooperative setting. Depending on the amount of group work they have done before this unit, you may structure their group participation in a variety of ways. If they have not done much work in small groups, you may find yourself spending time in the first few sessions conveying clear expectations about their group work. If your students have a history of working in groups, this will be more automatic. It takes time to develop these skills, even when the group work is interesting and appealing.

The size of working groups is important; for this unit the most effective groups

usually have two or three (occasionally four) members. Larger groups seem to limit the participation of the quieter students. Find the size that works best to support good discussion and thoughtful listening.

As you plan your class sessions, think about how you want to group students for small-group work. You may want to establish groups for the entire unit, or create new groups for each investigation. Some teachers form groups randomly, using counting-off methods or by having students select numbers from a container. Others group students in order to mix personalities or other student attributes. Still others group by convenience (all those sitting near each other). However you decide to group, make sure your students are clear about their groups and their roles as group members.

Materials

Students need materials to represent their data during their investigations. These range from Unifix cubes to pencil and paper to computer software. What is most important is that students are able to construct multiple views of the data quickly and easily and that they do not become bogged down in drawing and coloring elaborate graphs (which are appropriate only at the very end of an investigation when students are ready to "publish" their findings).

Any material that can be moved easily and rearranged quickly offers possibilities for looking at data. For example, students might write or draw their data on *index cards* (or any paper rectangles); then these can be arranged and rearranged. *Unifix cubes* (or other interconnecting cubes) are another good material for making representations throughout the grades. We have found that *stick-on notes* (such as Post-it notes), with each note representing one piece of data, are an excellent material for making rough drafts of graphs. They can be moved around easily and adhere to tables, desks, paper, or the chalkboard. *Pencil and unlined paper* should always be available for tallies, line plots, and other quick sketch graphs.

Calculators

Calculators should be available, if possible, throughout the activities. Their use is specifically suggested in some of the investigations. It is no secret to students that calculators are readily available in the world and that adults use them often. But many students do not know how to use a calculator accurately, do not check their results for reasonableness, and do not make sensible choices about when to use a calculator. Only through using calculators with appropriate guidance in the context of real problems can they gain these skills.

Computers

Computers are a key tool in data analysis in the world outside of school. Graphing software, for example, enables scientists and statisticians to display large sets of data quickly and to construct multiple views of the data easily. Some software for the elementary grades allows this flexibility as well. A finished graph made by the computer may, for some students, be an appropriate illustration for a final report of their findings. But keep in mind that students also make interesting and creative graphs by hand that would not be possible with the software available to them. Other computer software, including software for sorting and classifying and data base software, is particularly useful for some data analysis investigations. Where the use of a software tool would particularly enhance a data analysis investigation, recommendations for incorporating its use are made in the text and noted at the beginning of the session.

Home-school connections

Many opportunities arise in data analysis investigations for communicating with parents about the work going on in the classroom and for including them as participants in your data investigations. When you begin this unit, you may want to send a note home to parents explaining that students will be studying data analysis in their mathematics class and that, from time to time, parents can be of assistance in helping students collect data from home. Parents or other family members often provide an available comparison group.

Studies of age, family size, height, and so forth can be extended to include parents. If students are studying their own families, they may be interested in collecting comparison data about their parents' families. Including parents and other significant family members as participants in your data analysis investigations can stimulate their interest and enthusiasm for the work students are doing in school and, at the same time, help students see that the mathematics they do in school is connected to their life outside of school.

Interdisciplinary connections

Many teachers find ways to connect the data analysis experiences students have in mathematics to other areas of the curriculum. Data analysis is, after all, a tool for investigating phenomena of all kinds. The same approaches that students use in this unit can be called on for an investigation in science or social studies. Making these connections explicit and helping students transfer what they have learned here to new areas will give them an appreciation of the usefulness of mathematics throughout the curriculum. ■

MIDDLES, MEANS AND IN-BETWEENS
UNIT OVERVIEW

Statistics: Middles, Means, and In-Betweens is a unit of study for fifth and sixth graders who have already had experiences with collecting, organizing, and interpreting data, such as those provided in *Statistics: The Shape of the Data.*

Although the unit begins with investigations in data analysis similar to some that students may have done in earlier grades, the investigations quickly become more complex. In *Statistics: Middles, Means, and In-Betweens*, students:

▼ collect, represent, and analyze real data

▼ compare data about different groups

▼ use the median and mean as part of their descriptions of data sets

▼ investigate the mathematical relationship between the mean and the data

▼ interpret the mean and median as characteristics of a data set that give some, but not all, information about the data

How to use this unit

Like all of the Used Numbers units, *Statistics: Middles, Means, and In-Betweens* is organized into investigations that may extend from one to five class sessions. To cover the entire unit requires approximately 17 class sessions of about 45 minutes each. Pursuing any of the options and extensions that are provided will make the unit somewhat longer. Teachers who have used this unit have found that a schedule of 2–3 sessions per week works best to maintain continuity while allowing enough time for reflection and consolidation between sessions. The activities are sequenced so that students move gradually from more straight

forward to more complex investigations. The investigations are grouped into three parts:

▼ **Part 1: Describing, summarizing, and comparing data**
Raisins and more raisins
Heart throbs
The Paper Clip Game

▼ **Part 2: Understanding and using the mean**
The mean: Another kind of middle
Comparing sets of cereal data
Means in the news

▼ **Part 3: A project in data analysis**
Questions about work

The three parts work well as a single five- to six-week unit. Some teachers have substituted this unit for their textbook chapters on graphs or data. Others have used it late in the year as a way to consolidate students' mathematical learning, knowing that it brings together concepts in estimation, computation, graphing, and statistics in a problem-solving context. The parts can also be spaced over the entire school year. For example, some teachers use Part 1 in September to start off their work in mathematics. They return to Part 2 in January and use Part 3 in May when students have been together for most of the school year and are more able to work independently. Within each part, it is important that 2–3 sessions take place each week so that the experiences build on each other, allowing students gradually to acquire skills and understanding in data analysis.

Planning the investigations

In this book, you will find four types of information for each investigation:

Investigation overview. This section includes (1) a summary of the student activity, (2) materials you will need for the investigation and any special arrangements you may need to make, and (3) a list of the important mathematical ideas you will be emphasizing. Plan to look carefully at this overview a day or two before launching the investigation.

Session activities. For each session, you will find step-by-step suggestions that outline the students' explorations and the teacher's role. Although suggestions for questions and instructions are given, you will of course modify what you say to reflect your own style and the needs of your

students. In all cases, the teacher's words are intended to be guidelines, not word-for-word scripts. Plan to read through this section before each session to get the general flow of the activities in your mind.

Dialogue Boxes. The Dialogue Boxes illustrate the special role of discussion in these investigations and convey the nature of typical student-teacher interactions. Examples are drawn from the actual experiences of classes that have used these investigations. They call attention to issues that are likely to arise, possible student confusions and difficulties, and ways in which you can guide and support students in their mathematical thinking. Plan to read the relevant Dialogue Boxes before each session to help prepare for interactions with your students.

Teacher Notes. These sections provide important information you will need about the mathematical concepts to be presented and other aspects of the investigations. Here you will find explanations of the processes of sorting, collecting, and analyzing data, including ways to represent data and how and when to introduce certain mathematical ideas. The Teacher Notes are listed in the con-tents because many are useful as references throughout the unit, not just where they first appear. You might plan to read them all for background information before starting the unit, then review them as needed when they come up in particular investigations.

Goals for students

The "Important mathematical ideas" listed in the overviews of each investigation highlight the particular student goals for those sessions. Once goals are introduced in one part of the unit, they continue to be developed through experiences in later investigations. The major goals introduced in each part of *Statistics: Middles, Means, and In-Betweens* are as follows:

Part 1: Describing, summarizing, and comparing data

Describing the shape of the data. Students look at data sets and describe the important features of the data and the overall shape of how the data are distributed: the range of the data, where data are clustered, where they are spread out, what is typical of these data.

Making comparisons among different sets of data. Summarizing and describing individual data sets allows students to make comparisons among different data sets. Having an idea of what's typical of each data set is particularly useful in comparing data sets of different sizes.

Using the median as a landmark in the data. As students compare data sets, they will not only look at the overall shape of the distributions, but they will want to capture a typical or representative value for each data set by using some measure of the middle or center of the data. There are different ways of capturing the middle of the data; one is the median, the value that divides the data set in half.

Part 2: Understanding and using the mean

Understanding that the mean is a particular kind of "middle" or "balance point." Students usually learn about the mean when they are taught the computation algorithm "add all the numbers and divide by the number of numbers." In these activities, they develop an understanding of the mean as a number that describes a kind of middle or balance point in the data, a point that can be estimated without any reference to the algorithm.

Estimating the location of the mean. Estimating the value of the mean is an important part of describing any set of data. By constructing sets of data for a given mean and by estimating the mean for a given set of data, students get a feel for the way in which the mean and the data are related.

Understanding that many different data sets may have the same mean. Each data set has only one mean that describes it. However, there are many different data sets that could be constructed with identical means. These data sets can be very different from each other. One data set might be flat, with the same number of data points at each value. Another might have a tall middle, with most of the data clustered around the mean. Still another may be bumpy, with clumps of data on each side of the mean. Despite the differences, it is still possible that the same mean describes each set.

Using middle values to compare data sets. Students use means and medians to describe and compare data. Averages like means and medians are useful because they convey information about the data they represent in an abbreviated form. Just as we sometimes want a brief summary of an event, rather than a blow-by-blow account, we often want an overall sense of the data without knowing every individual value.

Comparing the median and mean as summaries of the data. Sometimes the median and mean give similar information about a set of data. At other times they can be quite different. While the median gives the value that divides the data set in half, the mean describes the point where all the data "balance." By looking at the mean and the median in the context of real data, students can decide how well they think these measures describe the data as a whole.

Using the mean in the context of other information to describe a data set. The mean tells us something important about the relationship between the data and the balance point of the data. However, the mean gives no information about the shape of the data, their range, or where the clumps and holes might be. For example, we cannot tell from the mean whether all the data are grouped close to the mean or whether they are quite spread out.

Interpreting a given mean when we do not have access to the data. As consumers of statistics, we are often confronted by average values—in the newspaper or other places—with no additional information. Understanding what the mean and the median do and do not tell about the data is a key skill if students are to become responsible citizens who can use statistical information critically and carefully.

Part 3: A project in data analysis

Defining what is being investigated. The first phase in data analysis is defining the question, deciding what data are needed, how they will be collected, and from whom.

Organizing, analyzing, and looking for patterns in the data. Students organize their data in order to interpret and find patterns in them. Data do not come pre-packaged; they need to be organized and categorized in a way that makes sense. It is important for the students to make their own decisions about how to organize the data, even if their approach is different from one adults might take.

Using measures of "typicality" as ways of describing more complex data. Students use their entire repertoire of skills for describing the shape of the data, including various methods of looking at typicality. In comparing sets of data, indicators of typicality, such as the median or mean, are especially useful ways to summarize data.

Building theories based on the data.
Identifying patterns is the heart of the process of data analysis. Careful examination of data helps students learn to use evidence to formulate hypotheses and theories. Throughout the final project, students are encouraged to view the data from different perspectives in order to address their own questions. ■

BEFORE YOU BEGIN . . .

Although this unit has no specific prerequisites, it assumes that students are in grade 5 or 6 and have already done some work with data analysis. Students undertaking this unit of study should be familiar with the processes of collecting, displaying, and interpreting real data. Appropriate experiences are provided by an earlier unit in the Used Numbers series, *Statistics: The Shape of the Data.*

The first investigation in Part 1, which involves counting the number of raisins in a box, repeats part of an investigation that appears in *Statistics: The Shape of the Data.* This activity serves to reacquaint students with collecting and recording data, making sketch graphs such as line plots, describing and summarizing data, using the median, and making predictions based on their data. If students have done this activity before, you may want to ask for predictions based on their previous experience. However, by the second session, students are undertaking more complex analysis than was required in the earlier unit. Now they

compare their own data with two other data sets, describe the differences among the data sets, and develop theories about what might account for these differences.

Family-size data, collected and analyzed in two earlier units in the series, is also revisited in this module, but here students use this familiar data in new ways as they work toward an in-depth understanding of using the mean to describe their data.

As you begin this unit, start collecting newspaper and magazine articles that use the idea of average. Students will also enjoy collecting and bringing in examples of averages that they encounter. You will put these averages to good use during the final investigation in Part 2, *Means in the news.*

Another average you will work with in Part 2 is the average amount of sugar in different types of cereal. Well in advance of this activity, start a collection of empty cereal boxes. You will need at least 30 boxes, representing both sugary and nonsugary cereals. ■

STATISTICS Middles, Means, and In-Betweens

PART 1
Describing, summarizing, and comparing data

RAISINS AND MORE RAISINS

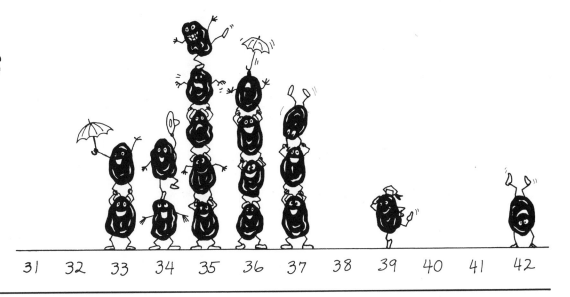

31 32 33 34 35 36 37 38 39 40 41 42

INVESTIGATION OVERVIEW

What happens

Students count the number of raisins in small boxes of raisins (one box for each student). They share methods of organizing, examining, and interpreting their data. Following this activity, students compare other sets of data (provided) from different samples of small boxes of raisins. They invent ways to compare data and also use the median as a way of making comparisons. Students use line plots as well as their own representations to help them describe and compare distributions of raisins.

The activities take two class sessions of about 45 minutes each.

What to plan ahead of time

▼ Anticipate students' inclination to use the averaging algorithm, but discourage them from using it. For suggestions on helping students focus on describing the data, rather than using the algorithm, read the Teacher Note, *The need for data description* (page 14).

▼ Provide small boxes of raisins (the half-ounce size), at least one for each student (Session 1). Have five extra boxes available for Session 2.

▼ Provide small stick-on notes and unlined paper for making sketch graphs (Session 1).

▼ Become familiar with making a line plot and finding a median. See the Teacher Notes, *Line plot: A quick way to show the shape of the data* (page 17) and *Finding and using the median* (page 18).

▼ Duplicate Student Sheet 1 (page 79) for each small group (Session 2).

Important mathematical ideas

Describing the shape of the data. While the focus of this unit is on finding and using "middles" in the data, describing the shape of the data is a critical and integral part of this work. Later, the *mean, median,* or *mode* will provide an important "summary statistic," but students must first understand what is being summarized. Students need to describe and find important features in the data. Help them gradually move from noticing individual features of the data ("Two boxes had 33 raisins, three boxes had 34 raisins") to describing the overall shape of the distribution ("Over half of the boxes had between 34 and 37 raisins").

Making quick sketches of the data. Graphs and tables are used not just for a final presentation of results, but also as working tools to represent data during the process of analysis. Support students' inventions of ways to display data quickly and clearly, and encourage them to build up a repertoire of useful "first draft" graphs such as line plots, tables, and tallies. In this session you will demonstrate a line plot, an especially useful sketch graph.

Making comparisons among different sets of data. Students use what they know about describing the shape of the data to make comparisons among different data sets. Students may initially compare ranges and modes of the different sets of data; they need to develop a variety of ways for comparing.

Using the median as a landmark to describe a set of data and for comparing two data sets. In order to use the median, students must understand the data it describes. The median is the value that divides the data set in half; that is, half of the data are less than or equal to the median value; half the data are equal to or greater than the median value. Further information is provided in the Teacher Note, *Finding and using the median.* ■

✎TEACHER NOTE
The need for data description

The three investigations in Part 1 of this unit review ways of describing, summarizing, and comparing data. Students need a great deal of experience in working with data before they are ready to think about how averages fit with these data. The Part 1 investigations provide varied opportunities to organize, represent, and interpret data. Students who have had little background with data analysis will need to spend a substantial amount of time with these introductory activities. If students have completed the earlier units in the Used Numbers series or have worked in other statistics curricula, you may want to spend less time on these first three investigations.

As you work through Part 1, students may suggest using the averaging algorithm ("add them all up and divide by the number of numbers") to find what's typical. This is an easy thing to do, but most students don't know why they are doing it. In Part 2, students will have a chance to construct for themselves what the average means. In the meantime, when they suggest using the algorithm, try to elicit their explanations of what an average is and how it will help solve the problem. You might ask, "How does it describe the data?" "What does it tell us about what's typical in this data set?"

Some students might suggest that the average is the number you get if you "evened out" the numbers of raisins, or pulse rates, or game scores. This is an important idea, and it is fine to encourage students to do this "evening out" if they suggest it. But discourage them from automatically applying the algorithm itself. They need to build an understanding of the average, and its relation to the data set, from their own experiences with data. ■

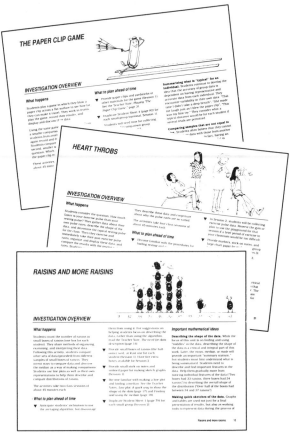

SESSION 1 ACTIVITIES

Introducing the unit

Suppose our principal asked me how much homework the students in this class do each week. Just listing everyone's hours for a week wouldn't be very helpful. The principal would want to know *in general* how much homework you do. It would also be interesting to me to know what's the most homework done by anyone in this class, and what's the least. We could see all of this information more easily if we organized and summarized the numbers that tell how many hours each of you spend on homework. Then, we could see patterns in the data. It's hard to describe large sets of data, so statisticians often use a few key numbers—like the range, the middle or median, and the average value—when talking about data. In this statistics unit, we will be thinking about how to summarize a set of data, or describe it with just a few numbers.

Considering the problem: Estimating the number of raisins

Throughout this unit, we'll be looking at different data sets and figuring out how to summarize and compare them. We'll start with some data about raisins.

Give a box of raisins to each student. Ask them to keep the boxes closed.

Does anybody have an idea about how many raisins there are in a box this size?

After students have made some estimates, let them open their boxes so they can see the top layer of raisins.

What do you think now? Do you want to revise your estimate?

Students may have a variety of ideas. Allow enough time for them to talk about these. Questions like the following might be used to elicit further discussion.

Why do you think there will be about [50]? Your idea is very different from Sammy's; how are you thinking about your estimate? Will the number of raisins in each box be the same or different? Why do you think so?

Collecting data: Counting raisins

Students open their boxes and count the raisins. They should write the number of raisins found in that box inside the top flap.

Recording and organizing the data: Sketch graphs

As students finish their counts, they report their data. Record the numbers in a list on the chalkboard, in whatever order they are reported.

If we wanted to organize these data so that we could see the whole set more clearly, what could we do?

Take a few suggestions from the students. Then have them work in pairs or in groups of three to decide on a form of sketch graph to organize the data quickly. Emphasize that this sketch is a rough draft; it need not be done meticulously. Once they have organized the data, each group should decide on and write down three important things they can say about their data.

Ask a few students to demonstrate their methods for organizing these data. Make sure that all the different types of representations they invent are demonstrated.

Several of you have used one good method for organizing data, called a *line plot*. Let's use that form for the rest of this investigation.

Organize the raisin data on a line plot large enough so that everyone can see it and in a place where it can be saved for the next session. See the Teacher Note, *Line plot: A quick way to show the shape of the data* (page 17).

Describing the data: What's the shape of these data?

What are some of the things you decided you could say about these data?

Help students express their initial ideas. Follow up with questions such as:

What else can you say about these data? Does anyone have another way to describe this representation? Suppose someone asked you, "About how many raisins are in a box?" What could you say?

See the Dialogue Box, *Describing the shape of the data* (following) for a sample discussion. This is a good opportunity to review the concept of median if students don't suggest it.

The median is a number that is used to describe the middle of the data—the location where half the boxes of raisins are below and half are above. Using the line plot, how would you find the median?

Help students see that they can count simultaneously from both ends of the line plot, counting off each piece of data until they locate the median number of raisins in a box.

The median tells us where the middle of the data falls. But it doesn't tell the whole story. What *don't* you know about this data set if you know only the median?

Help students notice other aspects of the data that are important. For example, the median doesn't tell how far the range goes: One raisin box could have 100, or the highest could be 45, and the median would stay the same. See the Teacher Note, *Finding and using the median* (page 18).

Developing theories: Making predictions

If we opened five more boxes of raisins, what is your best guess about how many raisins would be in them, based on the data we already have?

Elicit students' predictions and the reasoning behind their predictions. Encourage them to ask each other questions. In the next session they will see how close they came. At the end of the first session, allow students to eat the raisins. But keep the data for next time! ■

“”DIALOGUE BOX
Describing the shape of the data

The following discussion took place in a class doing the raisin investigation in *Statistics: The Shape of the Data*. This is the line plot they sketched to show how many raisins each student found in a box:

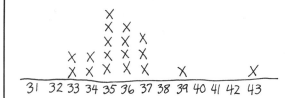

So what can you say about the raisin data? Let's hear a few of your ideas.

MARIA: Well, there are a lot at 35.

ALAN: There was only one at 39 and one at 43.

JANE: There are two at 33 and 34.

What else did you notice?

KAREN: Thirty-three is the lowest.

So no boxes had fewer than 33 raisins?

DAVID: Yeah. And 43 was the highest.

So the range was from 33 to 43. What else?

ANNIE: There's nothing at 38, 40, or 41.

Annie's noticing that there are a lot of holes

in this part of the data. Can anyone say any more about that?

SUE: Well, there's nothing at 31 or 32 either.

Yes, 33 is the lowest count and there's nothing below it. But this situation, that Annie noticed up here, is a little different. What can you say about that?

JESSIE: Mostly, the raisins go from 33 to 37, but sometimes you get something higher.

Can anyone add to that?

BEN: You'd be really lucky if you were the one who got 43!

In fact, mathematicians have a name for a piece of data that is far away from all the rest. They call it an *outlier*. An outlier is an unusual piece of data—sometimes it might actually be an error, but sometimes it's just an unusual piece of data. It's usually interesting to try to find out more about an outlier. Who had the outlier in this case?

CHRIS: I did. And I counted twice, and Kyle checked it, too, so I know it was 43.

JANE: Maybe he's got smaller raisins.

Any other theories about Chris's box?

MARY: Maybe it doesn't really weigh the same as the other boxes. Maybe too many raisins got dropped in when it was going through the factory.

[*Later*] . . .

So if someone asked you, "What's the typical number of raisins in a box?"—what would you say?

KIM: Well, I'd say 35.

[*Addressing the class as a whole, not just the student who answered*] **Why would 35 be a reasonable description of how many raisins are in a box?**

ALICE: Because the most boxes had 35.

Any other ways to say this? Or any different ideas?

ARRIE: Well, I wouldn't say just 35.

Why not?

ARRIE: Well, there's really not that much difference between 33, 34, 35, 36. They're all really close together. I'd say 33 to 37, 'cause the 39 and 43 aren't what you'd usually get.

So Arrie is saying he'd use an interval to describe the raisins, from 33 to 37, and Kim said she'd say 35 was typical. What do other people think about that?

☞ In this discussion, the class has moved gradually from describing individual features of the data to looking at the shape of the data as a whole. The teacher introduced the ideas of *interval*, *range*, and *outlier* because they came up in the discussion and were appropriate in describing these data. Throughout the conversation, the teacher tries to have students give reasons for their ideas and pushes them to think further by asking for additions or alternatives to ideas students have raised. ∎

✎ TEACHER NOTE
Line plot: A quick way to show the shape of the data

A line plot is a quick way to organize numerical data. It clearly shows the range of the data and how the data are distributed over that range. Line plots work especially well for numerical data with a small range, such as the number of raisins in a box.

This representation is often used as a working graph during data analysis. It is an initial organizing tool for beginning work with a data set, not a careful, formal picture used to present the data to someone else. Therefore, it need not include a title, labels, or a vertical axis. A line plot is simply a sketch showing the values of the data along a horizontal axis and X's to mark the frequency of those values in the data set. For example, if students have just collected data on the number of raisins in 15 boxes, a line plot showing these data might look like this:

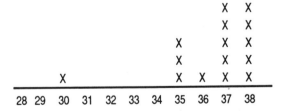

From this display, we can quickly see that two-thirds of the boxes have either 37 or 38 raisins. Although the range is from 30 to 38, the interval in which most data falls is from about 35 to 38. The outlier, at 30, appears to be an unusual value, separated by a considerable gap from the rest of the data.

One advantage of a line plot is that each piece of data can be recorded directly on the graph as it is collected. To set up a line plot, students start with an initial guess about what the range of the data is likely to be: What should we put as the lowest number? How high should we go? Leave some room on each end of the line plot so that you can lengthen the line later if the range includes lower or higher values than you expected.

By quickly sketching data in line plots on the chalkboard you provide a model of using such graphs to get a quick, clear picture of the shape of the data. ■

✎TEACHER NOTE
Finding and using the median

The median is an important landmark in a set of data. It is an *average* or a *measure of center* that helps summarize how the data are distributed. For example, the median age in the United States in 1985 was 31.5 years.* This statistic indicates that half the U.S. population was 31.5 years old or younger, while the remaining half of the population ranged in age from 31.5 years to the oldest living age. In other words, there are approximately as many people in the first three decades of life (0–30) as in the last, say, six decades of life (30–90). Notice that the median is *not* the middle of the range of the data; if the range of the data is from 0 to 90, the middle of this range would be 45 years. But the population is not spread symmetrically over this range. Just as many people are in the first third of the range as in the last two-thirds, so the median—the value that equally divides the data set—is at age 30 rather than age 45.

Another example is a data set showing the number of lifetime cavities of twenty-four 9-to-12-year-olds, illustrated at top right.

While the middle of the range is 5.5 (halfway between 0 and 11), the median is 2. Knowing

---

* Data from U. S. Bureau of the Census, Current Population Reports, Special Studies Series P-23, No. 150, *Population Profile of the United States: 1984/85*, U.S. Government Printing Office, Washington, DC, 1987.

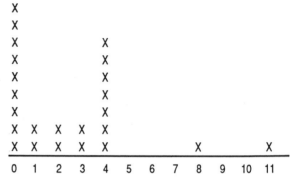

(Source: Dr. George W. McEachern III, DMD, Cambridge, MA.)

that the range is 0 to 11 and that the median is 2 tells us that there are as many children in the group with 0 to 2 cavities as there are children with from 2 to 11 cavities.

The median is the midpoint of the data set. If all the pieces of data are lined up in order, and one person counts from one end while another person counts from the other end, the value where they meet is the median value. If there is an odd number of pieces of data, the median is the value of the middle piece. If there is an even number of pieces of data, the median is the value midway between the two middle pieces.

Here's a line plot showing the number of raisins in 15 boxes, similar to those you made in the first investigation in this unit.

```
                                    X   X
                                    X   X
                        X           X   X
                        X           X   X
            X                       X   X   X   X
  ──────────────────────────────────────────────
  28  29  30  31  32  33  34  35  36  37  38
```

To find the median, imagine that we take all the values from the line plot and stretch them out in order:

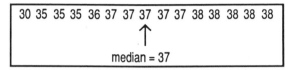

The middle value is 37, so the median is 37 for this set of data.

If the data set had contained one more box of 35 raisins, the data would have looked like this:

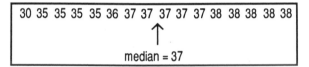

In this case, the median is between the two middle values; however, since the two middle values are the same, the median is still 37.

When the two middle values are *not* the same, as in the following data sets, the median is the value midway between the two middle numbers:

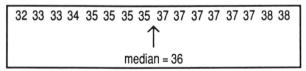

The median provides one landmark in the data, but it does not necessarily reveal all the important features of the data. For example, the fact that the median age in the United States is 31.5 years gives us some information about the shape of these data, especially because we bring to this piece of information some knowledge and experience about the context. That is, we know that ages range from birth to somewhere in the nineties or the low hundreds. We know that very few people reach ages beyond 90. So we can imagine to some extent what the age data look like. However, we still do not know, for example, what proportion of the 30-and-over group is over 65, or how many of the 0–30 group are in their teens. Experience with and knowledge of the context will help us interpret a statistic such as the median. However, for a data set to which we bring less of our own knowledge, the median or any other average, taken by itself, may not illuminate important aspects of the data. ∎

SESSION 2 ACTIVITIES

How accurate are our predictions? Adding more raisins

Call attention to the large line plot—showing the raisin data—that you created in Session 1. Review what students found last time, as well as their predictions concerning what would happen if five more boxes were opened.

Have the students open five more boxes of raisins and count them. Add these data to the line plot, using a different color or symbol to distinguish them from the original data.

How accurate were your predictions? What can you be pretty sure about if we open more boxes of raisins? About how many raisins are in a box?

Students may select different values to answer the question about the number of raisins in a box. The reasoning behind their answers is what's important. Students should be able to justify their choices.

Describing the number of raisins in several different samples

Now we're going to look at some additional data about raisins that were collected by students in fifth and sixth grade classes in two different schools. The data are all from half-

ounce boxes of raisins, which is the same size that you've been working with.

Hand out Student Sheet 1, *Samples of raisin data*. Ask students about their initial reactions to the data.

What do you notice about these data sets? How are they like or unlike what we found?

Students work together in small groups to analyze the new raisin data. They address the following questions:

▼ How do you suppose the students in these schools answered the question, "About how many raisins are in a box?" using their data?

▼ How does their data compare with our data? What can we say about how many raisins are in a box if we use all three sets of data?

▼ All of these samples came from boxes of the half-ounce size. Why do they look so different? What are your theories?

After working on these questions for a few minutes, representatives from each small group report what they found and explain their speculations about the differences. Focus students' attention on important features of the data and on the similarities and differences between the samples. Keep a list on the board of the students' suggestions about why the samples might look so different. For example, students might suggest that these are different brands of raisins or

that the raisins could be different sizes.

After students have discussed their theories about the differences, tell them this about the boxes: School A took their sample from a name brand of raisins, and School B from a store brand.

Extensions

If there are extra boxes of raisins, some students may want to count them and add the results to the data display. Or, you may want to keep the data posted and add to them periodically. Do these additional data change the shape of the data distribution in any way?

Students may want to compare boxes of raisins found in their local stores. They could make additional line plots, each showing a different brand. Which brand is the better value? They should keep in mind that more raisins could mean smaller raisins! ■

HEART THROBS

INVESTIGATION OVERVIEW

What happens

Students consider the question, How much faster is your exercise pulse than your resting pulse? They gather data about their own pulse rates, describe the shape of the data, and determine the typical resting pulse for the class. Then they exercise and immediately take their post-exercise pulse rates, organize and display these data, and compare the results with the resting pulse rates. Students invent their own ways of representing the data and also learn to use the stem-and-leaf plot.

Students are then given data sets with the resting pulse rates for newborn babies and for people who are 60–65 years old. They compare these data sets and determine how they are the same or different from their own resting pulse data. Then students are given the typical pulse rates for several animals.

They describe these data and conjecture about why the pulse rates are so varied.

The activities take four class sessions of about 45 minutes each.

What to plan ahead of time

▼ Become familiar with the procedures for finding resting and exercise pulse rates, as discussed in the Teacher Note, *Finding your pulse* (page 23).

▼ Provide a large clock with a second hand that is visible to the entire class (Sessions 1 and 2). Alternatively, digital watches can be used if at least half of the students have them, as students will work in pairs.

▼ Become familiar with making a stem-and-leaf plot. See the Teacher Note, *Stem-and-leaf plot: Another quick way to organize data* (page 24).

▼ In Session 2, students will be collecting exercise pulse data. Reserve the gym or plan to use the playground for that session if a brief period of exercise in your classroom would be too difficult.

▼ Provide markers, stick-on notes, and large chart paper for each small group for making sketch graphs (Session 3).

▼ Duplicate Student Sheets 2 and 3, (pages 80–81) for each student (Session 4).

Important mathematical ideas

Comparing a variety of data sets. A critical part of statistics is comparing data sets that may be quite different from one another. The pulse data presented in these sessions are quite varied, and provide opportunities for students to identify similarities and differences among the data sets.

Using "middles" to compare data sets. As students compare data sets, they look not only at the shape of the data, but also at the location of the median, mode, and modal "clumps" of data. At this stage, explore students' invented ways of looking at what's typical in addition to the median and mode.

Making comparisons. Sketch graphs make it much easier to compare two data sets. Encourage students to invent forms that make it possible for them to compare all important aspects of the data sets. Stem-and-leaf plots are introduced as one type of representation that facilitates such comparisons.

Finding patterns and relationships. It is intriguing to look for patterns and relationships in data sets. Simple relationships, like the one between exercise and pulse rate, are relatively easy to see. But it is also possible to identify more subtle patterns, such as the fact that smaller animals generally have faster pulse rates than larger ones. Students should be encouraged to look for relationships in their data and to conjecture about possible reasons for the patterns. ∎

SESSION 1 ACTIVITIES

Considering the problem

People who study sports medicine look at how exercise influences our health. They are especially interested in what exercise can do to keep a person's heart healthy. Researchers have found that people who do a lot of aerobic exercise—like running, swimming, biking, or other exercise that keeps them moving for at least a half hour at a stretch—have stronger hearts than people who don't exercise. In this next investigation, we're going to look at another question about exercise: How much faster does your heart beat when you're exercising than when you're resting?

Discuss what students have noticed about the effects of exercise on their heart rate. Ask them to speculate about how much faster their heart beats during exercise. A little faster? Twice as fast? Ten times faster?

Taking resting pulses

In order to determine how much faster your heart beats when you exercise, first you have to know what your resting heart rate is. That's how fast your heart beats when you are sitting still. What are your estimates?

Demonstrate the technique for finding your pulse, as discussed in the Teacher Note, *Finding your pulse* (page 23).

Ask for a student assistant to help you demonstrate the pulse taking technique. Decide how long you're going to count. Based on this decision, how will you get a rate per minute? Discuss students' ideas about how long to count and what to use as the multiplier for getting the per minute rate. In general, an interval of 10–30 seconds gives students time to get an accurate count.

Collecting the data

Students now pair up and begin taking pulses. One student serves as the timer while the other takes his or her own pulse. Each student should take several readings, and write down the results of each one.

Describing the data: Which number do we use?

Ask for a few volunteers to list their results on the board. Were each person's results always the same? If not, how do we decide which number to use? In this discussion, your role is to support students in finding a clear set of guidelines that can be applied consistently to each person in identifying resting pulse rates. See the Dialogue Box, *Which pulse is really mine?* (page 25).

Representing and describing the data

After students have decided which numbers they want to use, display the class data on a line plot on a large piece of paper. Students start by defining the range of values, which might be quite large. After you make the line, each student places his or her pulse rate on the chart with a stick-on note.

This is a good point at which to introduce a second way of representing the data: a stem-and-leaf plot.

When we're working with data that have a large range, it's sometimes hard to make a line plot, because the line has to be too long. Another type of representation that statisticians use in a case like this is called a stem-and-leaf-plot.

Demonstrate how to display the students' resting pulse rate data in a stem-and-leaf plot. See the Teacher Note, *Stem-and-leaf-plots: Another quick way to organize data*, (page 24).

List on the board all the "decades" represented in the pulse data. (For example, if your range was 48 to 87, write the numbers 4 through 8 in a column. Ask students to quickly give you their data again (or read the numbers from the line plot). List the "units" value for each piece of data on the right hand side of the line, as described in the Teacher Note.

Look at both representations—the line plot and the stem-and-leaf plot. What do the data tell you?

Bring into this discussion the idea that different types of representations make it easier to see different aspects of the same data. In this discussion, students explore the points where most of the pulse rates fall, any unusual or outlying values, and any clumps and holes in the data. They should also talk about what's representative in the data:

If you could use only one number to represent the class's resting pulse rate, what would it be?

Students should justify their choice of a number.

Preparing to take exercise pulse rates

In the next session, you will be collecting more data so you can answer the question, How much faster is your exercise pulse than your resting pulse? To get the new data, you need to exercise first. What kind of exercise would work?

Make a list of students' ideas about simple exercise (running, going up and down a couple of steps, doing jumping jacks) they could do to increase their heart rates. As a group, decide which exercise to do and how long to do it. Between 1 and 3 minutes is usually sufficient. Students may want to wear sneakers on that day. ■

✎ *TEACHER NOTE*
Finding your pulse

The best place to take a pulse is on the large (carotid) artery on either side of the neck. Use two fingers to press gently on the artery until you find your pulse.

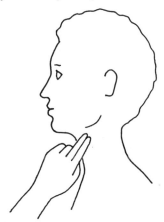

While students try to find their pulse using this method, walk around the room helping those who are having trouble. Make sure all students can find their pulse before the data collection starts.

Using the classroom clock for reference, discuss ways a minute could be divided to measure heart rate. Decide on the time interval to be used.

Share with students the following tips for obtaining accurate results:

▼ Silently mouth your counting instead of just thinking it; it's easy to lose track when counting in your head, but if everyone counts out loud, it gets confusing.

▼ Take more than one reading (for both resting and exercise rates) in case you miscount once.

▼ As you are getting ready to take your exercise pulse, feel for your pulse *before* you actually stop exercising so you will be ready to start counting immediately when the signal is given. ■

✎ TEACHER NOTE
Stem-and-leaf plot: Another quick way to organize data

The stem-and-leaf plot (also called a stem-plot) is an easy way to represent the shape of a data set. A stem-and-leaf plot works best for data with a range of several decades, since the plot is most frequently organized by tens.

For example, here are some data from a sixth grade class showing their pulse rates after one minute of exercise:

102, 180, 114, 120, 126, 174, 102, 132, 144, 126, 146, 162, 126, 174, 144

To make a stem-and-leaf plot of these data, we divide each value into tens and units. The tens become the "stem" of the plot, and the units are the "leaves":

```
10 | 2 2
11 | 4
12 | 0 6 6 6
13 | 2
14 | 4 4 6
15 |
16 | 2
17 | 4 4 4
18 | 0
```

In this plot, the first line shows two data points at 102. The second line shows a data

point at 114, and the third shows four data points: 120, 126, 126, and 126.

These data have been put in numerical order, allowing us to see more features of the distribution. This small set of data, despite having a large range, contains a number of identical values. The data are clustered between 120 and 146, with a significant cluster of data between 174 and 180. For this particular data set, a stem-and-leaf plot helps to show how the data are clustered. Because of the large range involved, these data would appear very spread out on a line plot. ■

❝❞DIALOGUE BOX
Which pulse is really mine?

Sammy, you got 60, 56, 64, and 36. Which one do you think we should use for the class data?

SAMMY: I'd say 36, because that was my best.

You mean your lowest? What do you think, should we use the lowest?

LISA: No, because Sammy's 36 isn't really right. He didn't start counting soon enough after I told him to start. It wasn't a fair try.

JACOB: Besides, I don't think you should count your lowest one even if it is fair.

Why not?

JACOB: It's not your real pulse, it's your slowest one, and we should be counting real pulses.

What do you mean by "real"?

JACOB: Well, the one that's kind of like the normal one I'd get, sort of the middle one.

Normal. That seems like an important idea. What's normal in our data?

SIRRAH: It isn't the high or the low ones. I got a real high one, 84, but I don't think that's right either. Because I think I got messed up counting.

What about 84? What other numbers did you get, Sirrah?

SIRRAH: I got 64, 64, and 72.

LISA: Those aren't very much like 84. **They're really different from the other numbers.**

JOHN: I think we should use the median of all the numbers we got. That's sort of the normal pulse.

JULIO: No, I think we should get rid of the messed-up tries first, then find the middle number.

Explain how you'd do that.

JULIO: Like I did two tries before Lisa and me got the starts and the stops to come out right.

So you could take out the numbers that weren't accurate?

JULIO: Yeah.

JOHN: I think we should use the middle number of the good tries. But I had 72, 72, 80, and 84, so there is no middle number.

MARTA: Well, you should use 72 because it came up the most.

(*Chorus of nos.*)

LISA: That one's lowest, and we decided not to use the lowest!

So if we want to go somewhere in the middle, how should we do it if there is no middle?

ERICA: You could just pick one of the numbers in the middle pair.

MARTA: Let's just do it like we did median before. If you have two numbers, go to the middle of those numbers.

So if you have an odd number, you choose the value in the middle. That's the median. If you have an even number, you find the middle pair and go in between these numbers. Do people agree?

JULIO: It's a little complicated, but I think it will work. ∎

SESSION 2 ACTIVITIES

Finding exercise pulse rates: On your marks, get set . . .

If you're going to the gym or playground to collect data, have students bring paper, pencil, and their watches. (If the gym has a large wall clock, that may be used in place of watches.)

Children again work in pairs. The procedure for finding an exercise pulse rate is slightly different.

Your pulse rate goes down very quickly after you exercise, especially if you're in good shape. Coaches and sports teachers often have people take their pulse immediately after they stop. They've also found that it's important to take your pulse for only a few seconds after you stop, so your heart rate doesn't have a chance to slow down. You'll take your pulse for 10 seconds as soon as you stop exercising.

Remind students about the type of exercise they decided upon and the length of time they decided to do it.

Collecting the data: . . . Go!

This part is fun. Remind students to exercise at a pace they can keep up for the whole time period. Ideally, students should have one practice turn at this, followed by a second chance to collect their data.

When you give the signal, one member of each pair will start exercising. Give a warning when it's almost time to stop, at which point the timers get ready to time and the exercisers get ready to count. When you give the signal "Find pulse!" exercisers immediately stop and locate their pulse. When everyone seems ready, tell the timers "Start!" The exercisers count until the timers signal "Stop" (after 10 seconds). Timers should record the results.

☞ **Important:** Sudden stopping of rapid exercise can sometimes cause faintness. Therefore, as soon as they have finished counting, exercisers should walk around until they catch their breath.

Students save their exercise pulse data for the next session. ■

SESSION 3 ACTIVITIES

Organizing and analyzing the data

Ask students for suggestions about how to calculate their per-minute exercise heart rates. When they've agreed on a method, record their individual rates on the board.

Post the stem-and-leaf display of the resting pulses next to the list of exercise pulse rates. During the rest of the session, students make new sketch graphs to help them compare the resting pulse rates with the exercise pulse rates.

We are going to figure our how much faster your exercise pulse rates are than your resting pulse rates. First we'll organize your data, then compare it.

Students form small groups of three or four members. Each group should have chart paper, markers, stick-on notes, and other construction material that might be helpful. The tasks for each small group are as follows:

1. Construct two sketches to show the two different sets of data. Use stem-and-leaf plots, line plots, simple tallies, or any other representation that helps display the data quickly.

2. Decide how to compare the data sets.

3. Try out the selected method for comparison. Are the results reasonable? If not,

try a different method.

4. Revise the sketch graphs, as necessary, to show the comparison as clearly as possible.

Reporting on the differences

Gather the class together and have a representative from each small group show the group's representation, explain their method of comparison, and answer the question, How much faster are our exercise pulse rates than our resting pulse rates? See the Dialogue Box, *Discussing the differences* (following).

Encourage students to explain their ways of comparing pulse rates, as well as their results. You will want to discuss each group's method for determining an answer. If no one brings up the median, suggest that it is one useful method for comparing groups, and work with the class to determine the median of each set of pulse rates. ■

"DIALOGUE BOX
Discussing the differences

How did your group find the answer to the question about differences in pulse rates?

JACOB: We got a median of 72 for our resting pulse and 150 for our exercise pulse. Then we subtracted the medians.

What does it tell you when you subtract the medians?

JACOB: Your pulse almost doubles when you exercise. Because 72 is what's typical for the resting pulse and 150 is what's typical for the exercise data. That's a big difference!

SIRRAH: Also, we found that the exercise pulses were more spread out than the resting pulses. The exercise pulses went from 110 to 180. But the resting pulses only went from 48 to 80, which is less.

So besides having different medians you had very different ranges in your data sets.

SIRRAH: Yeah, because our heart beats are all sort of the same when we're sitting around. But some of us are used to exercise, and others don't exercise so much. So there's a bigger range in our exercise data.

That's an interesting difference. What other ways did people have of thinking about the difference?

MARTA: We looked at the big clumps of data on our line plot. See, most of the resting pulse rates are around 64 to 72. And most of the exercise pulses are between 148 and 164.

SAMMY: But it's still pretty hard to tell what the differences are. We can tell a range for each time, but we can't tell an exact number.

LAUREN: We made a list of everyone's resting pulse. Then we made a list of everyone's exercise pulse. Then we subtracted out each pair. Like before and after. I was doing 84 resting and 126 after exercise. The difference was 42. We did all the pairs like that and we have a list of differences.

What can you tell from your list of differences?

LISA: For one thing, people are pretty different. Lauren's difference was only 42, but some people had differences over 100.

JULIO: Yeah, so then we wanted to see what the typical difference was. We made a list of all the numbers in order, and we found out that the median was 86.

The median?

JULIO: The median difference, from our list, between resting and exercise was 86 beats.

That falls in the range that Marta's group found, the range of 84 to 92.

ASHOK: It looks like most of us are finding the difference to be somewhere between the high 70s and the low 90s. ■

SESSION 4 ACTIVITIES

Developing theories: What do we know about typical pulse rates?

Hand out Student Sheet 2, *Pulse rates for two age groups*, giving data for newborn babies and people in the 60–65 age range. Discuss the shape of the data in each case. How do these data sets compare with each other, and with the students' own resting pulse rates? What is the typical pulse rate for people in each age group, and how different are they? Students should speculate about what might be affecting the differences in pulse rate. As students make their speculations, keep a running list of their theories on the board.

Finding patterns in animal data

Hand out Student Sheet 3, *Animal pulse rates*, with the animal pulse rate data arranged in a stem-and-leaf plot.

As a final activity, students work in small groups looking for patterns in the animal data. In general, what can they say about these pulse rates? What kinds of animals have higher resting pulse rates, and which ones have lower rates?

Suggest that students look for clusters of animals with similar pulse rates and see if they can determine what these animals have in common. If there is time, students may

want to write about the patterns they see, as other classes have done. See the Dialogue Box, *Writing about pulses* (following). Alternatively, they could simply report their findings to the class.

Extension: What determines heart rate?

In this investigation, students have done a good deal of speculation about factors that cause heart rates to vary. This activity could easily be extended into a science lesson dealing with size, age, and energy expenditure as factors affecting the pulse rates of various animals. An excellent student reference for follow-up activities is *Sportworks* by the Ontario Science Center (Addison-Wesley, 1988). This book is full of activities concerning cardiovascular fitness, and includes some nice data sets on pulse rates. ■

❝❞DIALOGUE BOX
Writing about pulses

Below are two writing samples from sixth graders who examined the animal pulse data. They found different patterns in the data and offered interesting explanations for these patterns.

▼ I noticed that the top was a range of 16–150 and there were 44 listed. But from 160–600 they weren't as clustered and there was a much bigger range. Most of the animals on the bottom half were birds, but only one on the top was. That bird was the ostrich. The animals that have the slower heart rate tend to have a heavier body weight. I also saw that there were no fish on the range from 160–600.

▼ I found out from the graph that the smaller animals have higher pulse rates. The bigger ones have slower pulse rates. Also if you take a land animal, air animal, and the sea animal, the sea animal will have the slowest pulse rate. Between two whale heart beats, the gull's heart beats 25 times! That's nine more times than a whale's heart beats in a minute! Between every two whale heart beats the mouse beats 37 times. ■

THE PAPER CLIP GAME

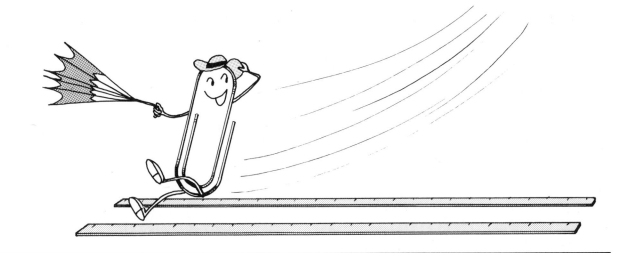

INVESTIGATION OVERVIEW

What happens

Students play a game in which they blow a paper clip across a flat surface to see how far they can make it travel. They work in teams, play the game, record their results, and display and discuss their data.

Using the same game, they gather data from a smaller comparison group—teachers, students from another class or grade—and again record and display these data. Students compare their own data to the second, smaller set of data, to answer the question, Which of these groups can make the paper clip travel the farthest?

These activities take two class sessions of about 45 minutes each.

What to plan ahead of time

▼ Provide paper clips and yardsticks or other materials for the game (Session 1). See the Teacher Note, *Playing "The Paper Clip Game,"* page 31.

▼ Duplicate Student Sheet 4 (page 82) for each small group (optional, Session 1).

▼ Students will need time for collecting data from the comparison group between Sessions 1 and 2.

Important mathematical ideas

Defining the way data will be collected. Students make decisions about how to collect the data, play the game, and judge the results. They determine how to define the rules of the game, as well as how to measure the results in a consistent manner.

Summarizing what is "typical" for an individual. Students continue to develop the idea that the accuracy of group data is dependent on having representative and accurate data from each individual. They encounter variability in their own data: "That time I didn't take a deep breath"; "She made me laugh just as I blew the paper clip"; "This was my first try." They consider what a typical distance would be for each student if several trials are permitted.

Comparing samples that are not equal in size. Students often believe that they cannot compare their data with those from another bigger or smaller group. In fact, having an idea of "what's typical" is very useful in comparing two different-sized groups. With different-sized groups, it is not possible to simply compare totals. Students invent fair ways of comparing the groups. ■

SESSION 1 ACTIVITIES

Introducing the game

Sometimes, you have to figure out the winner of a game when the sides aren't even. This can be tricky. What do you do when you have to count everybody's score—but the teams aren't equal in size? This is the kind of problem we're going to deal with in this investigation. We're going to devise a game that we'll call "The Paper Clip Game," and we'll compare our scores with those of a challenging team.

Describe the game as explained in the Teacher Note, *Playing "The Paper Clip Game,"* (page 31).

I have described the point of the game to you; now you need to develop procedures and rules to play the game. How do you want to play it?

Have a few students demonstrate the activity in order to surface questions and develop the procedures they will use to play the game. Questions that may emerge include:

> How should each of us blow the paper clip?
> Do we blow it from above or from the same level?
> How many tries should people get?
> How should we measure the distance the paper clip travels, especially if it travels at an angle?

As the group makes decisions about proce-dures, write them down on the board so that players can refer to them during the game.

An important part of this discussion is figuring out which trials "count." Everyone will have a chance to play several times. Do students want to keep only the best result? The most typical result? The best three? They should make this decision as a group and all follow the same procedures.

Collecting the data: Measuring the distance traveled

Students form teams of four to five members to play the game and collect the data for the class. While the teams aren't competing directly against one another, teamwork makes the activity move more quickly. Give each team a copy of Student Sheet 4, *Record sheet for paper clip scores*, or have them set up a similar sheet using notebook paper to keep track of how far the clip travels each time.

Representing, organizing, and describing the data

After the teams have finished, students display their results on a class line plot, perhaps using stick-on notes with a large sheet of chart paper. If you've decided to count a number of trials from each indivi-dual, the students might make a separate chart for each trial. Or you can make line plots such as "Our Best Tries" and "Our Typical Scores."

When the class plot is complete, examine the results. Encourage the students to look at clusters of data, gaps in the data, and unusual scores, and to try to describe the overall results.

Keep the class line plot (or other represen-tation of students' data) for Session 2.

Collecting more data: The challenge

With the students, identify a second group of people or "challengers" who will play the game following the same procedures that the students have established. This group might be another group of children in the school, teachers, or administrators. What's important is that the second group be *smaller* than your class.

Arrange to have the group come into your classroom to play the game. Be sure the class decides in advance the answers to these questions:

▼ How many times should the challengers get to practice?

▼ Which trial or data will we "count" for them?

The challengers could play the game during recess or after school. Students may be willing to let the other group use the honor system and score their own trials. They may find it acceptable for you to monitor the game. However, don't be surprised if a student monitor wants to be present! Use additional record sheets (Student Sheet 4 or similar charts) to keep track of the scores of the other group. ■

✎ TEACHER NOTE
Playing "The Paper Clip Game"

To play this game, students each blow a paper clip across a flat surface like a table or floor. One way to do this is to make a track out of two yardsticks, placed about two inches apart and parallel to each other. Players are positioned at one end of the track; they blow the paper clips from this end. Measure the distance traveled by checking the yardsticks. A few students may be able to blow the clips farther than a yard, in which case one yardstick can be moved for measuring purposes.

Students may want to experiment with different kinds of tracks for the paper clips,

or they may not want to use a track at all. You may want to try a couple of different options, then choose the version of the game that seems to work best for the class.

A variation of this game is "The Pencil Blowing Game." Pencils work better than paper clips on carpeted floors. In one version of this game that we observed, the students extended a measuring tape across the carpeted floor, then stood at one end and blew pencils along a path parallel to the tape. When making their measurements, they decided to count the end of the pencil that was closer to the tape.

The more that students are involved in decisions about the structure and rules for the game, the more interested they'll be in analyzing the outcomes! ■

SESSION 2 ACTIVITIES

Representing, organizing, and describing the new data

Students work in small groups, with each group having a copy of the record sheets from the challengers. They also need to see the line plot of their own data from Session 1.

The task for each small group is to compare how the class did (as a group) with how the challengers did. They make a sketch graph of each group's scores so they can compare the data from the two groups. Ultimately the question they address is, Which side won? The only rule is that they have to take into account the *entire group's* performance, not just the performance of the best player. When they report to the class, they will need to back up their decision with data.

Encourage students to look at the clusters of data, gaps in the data, and typical scores when making their comparisons.

Reporting to the class: Who won?

Each small group should report on their findings. As the groups present their results, it should become clear that different strategies for determining who won may lead to different winners! Expect students to give good reasons for choosing a particular strategy. They need to be clear about what

winning means and to explain their thoughts about determining which group won.

If all the groups come up with decisions in their own favor, ask:

If we were the challengers, is there any way we could argue that we won—and not this class? How would the data justify this different decision?

Extension

Write a class letter to the challengers explaining who you think won and why. Include copies of the data. Ask them to examine the data and write back with their opinion about the winner. ■

❝❞DIALOGUE BOX
Winners and losers

These students are discussing their line plots (see below) showing the scoring results when their class and a group of teachers as challengers played "The Paper Clip Game."

MARTA: We decided that our class won. We've got a lot more data in the 26–40 range. Plus our range is bigger. They don't have anyone higher than 32.

LAUREN: Also, they have two low scores that are less than 20. That's 20% of their scores. We have three low scores out of 19. That's less than 20%. So we win on the percentage of low scores. And we win on the percentage of high scores too. Because we have three high scores and they have only one.

So comparing the highs and lows made you think that you were the winners.

MARTA: Yeah, but it's actually pretty close.

Any other groups?

JACOB: First we looked at the medians. Ours is 23 and theirs is 23.5. But that's too close to call.

ASHOK: We looked at the modes. Ours is 24. Theirs is only 23. We win on that one.

LAUREN: But we have a mode at 20 too!

ASHOK: But we decided to count the highest mode.

JACOB: Then we subtracted their high score from our high score. That's a difference of 8 in our favor. Then we subtracted the low scores. That's a difference of 2 in *their* favor. But overall, we still have 6 extra points, when you subtract it out.

So your group also compared the highs and the lows, but a little bit differently than the other group. Anyone else?

SIRRAH: I hate to say it, but we did it a different way and we think the teachers won.

(*Gasps from the class.*)

How did you look at it?

SIRRAH: Well, if you look at the line plots we made, you can just see that theirs is sort of clumped in the 23-29 area. Ours is more spread out, and we have a lot more people in the 20-22 area.

ERICA: We think that their typical players are better than our typical players.

JULIO: Yeah, but the highs should count for something. Our best are better than their best!

ERICA: Our group decided to look at all of the scores. That seems fairest. And when you look at all the scores, I think the teachers won.

JULIO: Maybe they used smaller paper clips. Let's try it again.

I think maybe the teachers would be interested in this data. Let's give it to them and see who they think won.

LAUREN: But they have to be fair about it. They have to give us reasons!

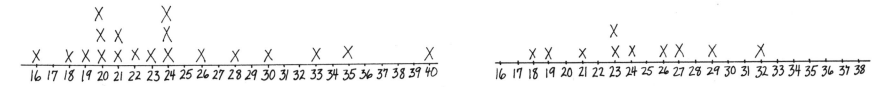

Our class – 19 kids

The 10 teachers

STATISTICS **Middles, Means, and In-Betweens**

PART 2
Understanding and using the mean

THE MEAN: ANOTHER KIND OF MIDDLE

INVESTIGATION OVERVIEW

What happens

Students explore the concept of *mean* as a particular kind of average, examining data sets about family size and about soda pop consumption.

In the first session, they imagine a class of students in which the mean family size is 4. They use stick-on notes, which they move around on a line plot, to demonstrate what the distribution of family size might actually be. In this session, they are introduced to a new way of thinking about the mean—that any deviation from the mean in one direction must be matched or "balanced" by an equal deviation from the mean in the other direction. Using this idea, students "undo" a mean by breaking it down into the values that could make up that particular mean.

In the second session, students bring in their own data about how much soda pop they

drink in a week and apply the same strategies for thinking about mean. The students are encouraged to look at small data sets, estimate where the mean might be, and examine the distances of the data from the mean to see where the balance point (the mean) is.

☞ During these activities, postpone the use of the algorithm for finding the mean (add up all the numbers and divide by the number of numbers) until it is introduced in the middle of Session 2. Even though your students probably know this formula, it is unlikely that they understand much about how the mean relates to the data. We have found that using the formula too early in these activities gets in the way of students' understanding of how to interpret and use the mean. Let students know that you are more interested in their reasoning about how the mean and the data are related than in precise calculation, and that in these investigations

estimation is much more important than exact results. See the Teacher Note, *The limitations of learning the averaging algorithm* (page 49).

The activities take two class sessions of about 45 minutes each.

What to plan ahead of time

▼ Become familiar with the important mathematical aspects of the mean and its relationship to the data as described in the Teacher Note, *How the mean fits the data* (page 42). You will not use all this information directly with your students, but it is important background information for you.

▼ Provide small stick-on notes and large squared paper or a similar material (Session 1).

▼ If possible, plan to allow time (as much as one week) for students to collect data about their soda-pop consumption (before Session 2).

▼ Duplicate Student Sheet 5 for each student (Session 2).

▼ Provide calculators (Session 2).

Important mathematical ideas

Estimating the location of the mean. Examining data and estimating the value of the mean is an important part of describing any set of data. Most of us have very little experience with this skill. Initially, students may not even realize that the mean is one kind of "middle" number and, consequently, always falls within the range of the actual data set. Constructing sets of data for a given mean, as well as estimating the mean for a given set of data, provide students with a feel for the relationship between the mean and the data.

Understanding that the mean is a particular kind of "middle" or "balance point." Students usually learn about the mean when they are taught the computation algorithm "add all the numbers and divide by the number of numbers." In these activities, they develop an understanding of the mean as a number that describes a kind of middle or balance point in the data—a point that can be estimated without any reference to the algorithm. It is important for students to understand that the mean represents a particular kind of center in the data before they use a memorized algorithm.

Understanding that many different data sets may have the same mean. Each data set has only one mean that describes it. However, there are many different data sets that could be constructed with identical means. These data sets can be very different from each other. One data set might be flat, with the same number of data points at each value. Another might have a tall middle, with most of the data clustered around the mean. Still another may be bumpy, with clumps of data on each side of the mean. Despite the differences, it is still possible that the same mean describes each set. For this reason, the mean alone does not give enough information about the data. ■

SESSION 1 ACTIVITIES

Introducing the problem: A new kind of middle

You often hear about a statistic called the "average." What are some kinds of averages you know about?

As students make suggestions, you might give additional examples of averages from your school, or community, or from newspaper articles you have collected.

A lot of you have learned how to calculate an average called a "mean."

Remind students or have them volunteer what they know about the "add-up-all-the-numbers-and-divide-by-the-number-of-numbers" formula.

The "add-'em-all-up" formula you learned is for a special kind of average called the "mean." You already know about another kind of average—the median—which we used in the raisins investigation and the pulse rate comparisons. The mean is a different kind of middle and it's harder to understand than the median. Unfortunately, most of us just memorize the "add-em-all-up-and-divide" formula, but we never really understand what the mean is. So we're going to forget about the formula for awhile and look at some ways to really know what kind of middle the mean is.

Constructing data for a mean: If the average family size is 4 . . .

Usually when people say "average," they are thinking of the mean. One average—or mean—that we often hear about is the average family size. When the census was taken in April 1990, one of the things the census forms asked about was the size of everyone's family.

In one school where the students figured out the average family size in their school, the average came out to about 4. If the mean family size in their school was 4, what do you think this would tell us about the families in their school?

Ask students to describe what they think a mean of 4 would suggest about the families in this school. Does that mean that there are a lot of families with 4? But could there also be a lot with 3 or 5 people? Would there be any with 1? 2? 8? Encourage them to consider what's reasonable based on their own experience. For example, a family of a student has at least two members in it (the student and a parent or guardian), so there can be no families of 1 in these data. Also, there is an upper limit to family size. Family sizes much beyond 6 are not as common as family sizes in the range of 2 to 6 members. Students' knowledge of themselves and their friends will give them a sense of what family sizes might be.

Show students six towers, each made with 4 interconnecting cubes or blocks.

These towers show six families, each with 4 people in the family. If we had enough towers for all the students in the school and every single tower had 4 cubes in it, then there would certainly be an average family size of 4! But, as you've all said, that isn't very likely.

Give each group of two or three students a set of six towers, with 4 blocks in each tower. Ask each team to rearrange the cubes to make a more realistic set of six families with a mean family size of 4. Some arrangements might be:

$$2, 3, 3, 4, 4, 8$$
or
$$3, 3, 4, 4, 5, 5$$

Discuss students' constructions of family data. Does it seem reasonable to say that the mean or average family size is 4 in each of their constructions?

Constructing data on a line plot: Focus on distance from the mean

Draw a line plot on the board. Use stick-on notes or chalk marks to show the six families with 4 members. Stick-on notes work well here, since you will be moving the points on the line plot.

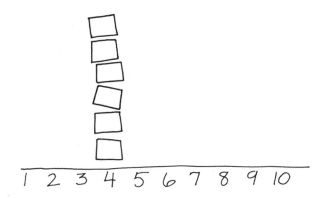

Each of the stick-on notes on this line plot represents one family. There are six families, and each family has 4 people. This is one way of thinking about an average family size of 4, but we know that is not the way it really is. Not every family really has 4 people.

One way that statisticians think about the mean is that it's a number on a line plot like this one, and the distances of all the data on one side of the average have to be the same as all the distances of the data on the other side.

For example, if we moved one family over so it had 3 members, what would we have to do to the other side to make the average come out to 4?

Usually students suggest moving one data point out to 5 in order to balance the 3. Ask them why this works. Repeat the procedure of moving one data point and asking the students to make the necessary adjustment with a second data point.

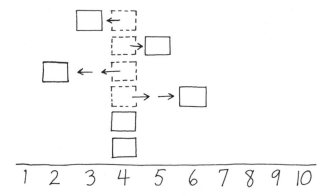

This section of today's session should proceed slowly, so that all students have a chance to grasp this idea of balancing data on each side of the mean. This idea will probably be a new one for most students. Do several examples, as shown above, until students seem to be comfortable with balancing pairs.

Sometimes there might be a large family. For example, one family might have 8 people. What do we do now? How can we keep the average at 4?

Moving a data point farther away from the mean necessitates a different kind of adjustment. You need to move more than one data point to "balance off" the large family. Allow students to think out how they can balance the family of 8 with more than one piece of data. See the Dialogue Box, *Beyond pairs* (page 41).

Constructing more data to fit the mean: A class with a family size of 4

Students work in small groups to make a line plot, with stick-on notes, showing a mean of 4 for an entire class. In other words, they are going to make up a fantasy class of, say, 20 or 25 students (each group need not use exactly the same number) with an average family size of 4. Encourage students to use their own strategies as well as any strategies that may have come up during the discussion. As you walk around the room, you may find some groups employing very simple strategies that work quite well (e.g., 8 families of 3, 8 families of 4, and 8 families of 5). These strategies are fine, but you may want to challenge some groups further by moving one or more of their families to a different position (for example, move a 4 to 9, a 5 to 7). After you have moved a data point, can students adjust the distribution to make it come out so that the average is still 4?

As you circulate among the groups, ask students to explain their strategies:

How did you construct the data so the average turns out to be 4? Do the data on one side of the mean balance the data on the other side? How do you know that what you did works?

Expect students to prove that their distribution works by showing that all the data on one side of the mean are the same total distance away from the mean as all the data on the other side of the mean.

Introducing a new problem: How much soda pop do you drink?

For our next data analysis session, we are going to take a look at the average amount of soda pop all of you drink in a week. Let's decide what data you should bring in.

Discuss with your students how they can collect data to answer the question, How many regular-sized cans or bottles of soda pop have you drunk in the last week? They will need to decide how to define a week (from when to when) and how they will count so that their data are as accurate as possible. They will need to decide what counts as soda pop: Should natural soda, carbonated fruit juices, or spritzer be included? Students might bring up the possibility that the "real" data could be different from what students report; that is, students might under-or over-report what they actually drank. Talk about this, and the importance of being as accurate as possible in their reports.

Depending on your schedule, you may want to pause here for a week while your students collect the data. Or you and your students may decide to rely on memory for the past week.

Extension

Students may want to investigate the actual family size in their own class or school. We have not included this investigation here since it is used in two of the other upper grade units in this series, *Statistics: The Shape of the Data* and *Statistics: Prediction and Sampling*. The family-size investigation is a very rich one in which students first have an extended discussion to decide how they will count family members, then collect, display, and compare data. There are many opportunities for comparing data among different classes in the school or between generations. (How big are our families? How big were the families our parents grew up in?) If students have not previously worked with family size—or even if they have—they might enjoy several additional sessions in which they collect and explore real data. ■

❝❞ DIALOGUE BOX
Beyond pairs

Working on the board with a line plot and stick-on notes (as shown earlier), the teacher moves one stick-on from 4 to 8.

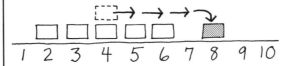

Now we have a stick-on note on 8 for a family with 8 members. What has that done to the average?

BEN: Well, it's gotta be higher than 4 now.

How could we change some other numbers to get it back to 4?

MARTA: Maybe put one really low, like at 1.

JULIO: No, that won't work because you couldn't be a family of 1 at this school— you'd be living by yourself. That's against the law until you're 16 or something.

ERICA: There was someone in a show I saw who did live by herself, but she didn't tell anyone.

LISA: Hey!—1 wouldn't work anyhow. One's not as far away from 4 as 8 is. To make it work, you'd have to have a dot at 0.

JULIO: But that wouldn't be a family at all!

So 1 wouldn't work and neither would 0. What can we do about it? If we were making the whole data set, putting on as many stick-on notes as we'd like, how could we make the average come back to 4? In your discussion before, some of you said there could be a few large families, but the average could still be 4. So how could that work here?

MARTA: Maybe there's a way of doing it if you had a few kids with small families.

Tell us more about your idea.

MARTA: Ben's family's big, but I only have 2 in my family and John only has 3, and Sammy has 2. So that kind of makes it even.

So a few small families, along with one big family, might balance out to an average of 4? Someone come up and put some data on the chart to show how it would work.

JUANA [*putting stick-on notes at 2, 3, and 2*]: That would work.

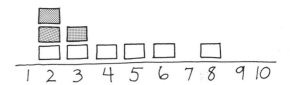

SAMMY: Yeah, but you don't need the 3 up there, because it's enough just to have two families of 2.

MARTA: Sammy is right. You don't need John's family because the other two families are each 2 away from the average. That

[Dialogue Box continued]

makes 4 altogether. The 8 is also 4 away from the average, so it's the same on both sides.

That's an interesting way to think about it. That strategy of making the total distance come out the same on either side works really well.

☞ In this discussion, the students are thinking about a complex strategy for balancing the big family and making the average come out to 4. The teacher encourages qualitative strategies in the beginning (putting lots of small families on the left side to balance one big family). Some of the students see that the balancing can be done in a more precise way, and they work out a way to make the sides exactly equivalent. ∎

✎ TEACHER NOTE
How the mean fits the data

Most of us have not had experiences that help us think about how the mean fits the data. For example, if the average number of raisins in a box is 35, what does that tell us? We know something about the algorithm for finding the average: adding up all the numbers and dividing by the number of numbers. But why would anyone want to do this? What does this particular number tell us about the data?

Although we rarely think of it this way, the mean is really a place where all the data "balance" in a precise way. It is a kind of middle point that has to do with how the data are spread out. For example, here's a distribution of data collected from ten boxes of raisins:

```
                X
  X     X       X
  X     X   X   X   X   X
  33    34  35  36  37  38
```

In this distribution, 35 is the mean. If you imagine the number line as a balance beam, 35 is the point where you can put a fulcrum. The values to the right and left of 35 balance each other so that the beam remains level.

There are different combinations of data that would give a mean of 35. In the following two distributions, the mean or balance point is still 35:

```
  X   X
  X   X   X   X   X   X
  33  34  35  36  37  38
```

```
  X   X
  X   X           X   X   X
  33  34  35  36  37  38
```

How does this work? Without actually having a balance beam and something to represent the raisin boxes, how can we "see" that the balance in these pictures is at 35?

What is important to watch is not the values themselves (33, 34, 35, and so on), but *how far away the values are from the balance point*. The balance point is the point where the total distances on one side of the fulcrum are the same as the total distances on the other side. Here's the first line plot again with the distances of each piece of data from the mean marked:

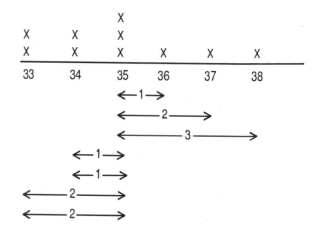

Several values are below the mean. The sum of their differences from the mean is 6. Other values are greater than the mean, and the sum of their differences from 35 is also 6. This will always be true. The mean is the balance point where the total differences above the mean equal the total differences below the mean. In statistics, this relationship is described by saying that "the sum of the deviations on one side of the mean must equal the sum of the deviations on the other side."

Students can begin thinking about this relationship by constructing sets of data with the mean exactly in the middle of the set and with pairs of values balanced around it. For example, suppose the average price of a bag of potato chips is $1.38. Here are three possible sets of data that give an average of $1.38:

1. $1.28, $1.38, $1.48

2. $1.36, $1.37, $1.38, $1.39, $1.40

3. $1.30, $1.34, $1.42, $1.46

In each instance, every value is exactly balanced by another. In the first example, $1.28—10 cents lower than $1.38—is balanced by $1.48—exactly 10 cents higher.

Going up a certain distance from the mean, then down the same distance, is a powerful strategy for beginning to understand how the mean sits in the middle of the data. Many students talk about this as "balancing the data" around the mean. This simple strategy is crucial for understanding the relationship between the mean and the data it describes.

Of course, a real data set is generally not perfectly symmetrical. The raisin data shown above, for example, are not balanced precisely in pairs. Gradually, students extend balancing by pairs to working with data sets that are larger and not perfectly symmetrical. For example, in a data set of potato chip prices where the mean is $1.38, it is possible for the data to be "balanced" around this value even when there are an odd number of data points and the mean is not one of the prices. One student constructed the following data set, which has a mean of $1.38:

$1.33, $1.33, $1.48

Instead of going down 10 cents from the mean to $1.28 to balance the $1.48, she "went down 5 cents times 2," using two values of $1.33 to balance the $1.48 and still give her an average price of $1.38:

```
     X
     X                        X
 ───────────────────────────────────
   1.33        1.38        1.48
              ←———— 10 ————→
     ←—— 5 ——→
     ←—— 5 ——→
```

There are many ways she could have done this, as long as the values less than $1.38 were the same total distance away from the mean as the values higher than $1.38. This set also works:

$1.31, $1.35, $1.48

Once students catch on to the basic idea, they find it challenging to construct many different data sets that meet the criteria for relating the data to the mean. ■

A note on terminology: "Average" or "mean"?

In everyday conversation we use the terms *average* and *mean* interchangeably. When you read in the paper that the "average amount of ice cream consumed in the United States is 45.14 pints per year per capita," the word *average* refers to the mean. However, there are actually many kinds of average. An average is any statistic used to summarize the center or middle of the data. The median is one kind of average; the mode—the most frequent value in the data—is also considered to be an average. In this section, we use *average* to refer to the mean. We hope that students leave this unit aware that there is more than one kind of average, but they should understand that when people, newspapers, or even their textbooks or tests refer to "average," the mean is generally intended unless another statistic is specifically mentioned. ∎

SESSION 2 ACTIVITIES

Describing a small set of data: Estimating the mean

Hand out a copy of Student Sheet 5, *What's the average?*, to each student.

You've been bringing in some data about soda pop, and now we're going to find out about the average amount of soda pop members of our class drink. But before you work with your own data, I'd like you to take a look at the data on this sheet. Looking at the graph on the left, what can you say about the amount of soda that these five students drank in a week?

After students have described the data, ask them to draw lightly in pencil a vertical line showing about where they would estimate the mean of these data to be. Then ask students about the reasons for their estimates. Expect comments such as, "I think it's about 6 because that's in the middle between 0 and 13," or "I think it would be closer to 8, because even though the 0 is really far down, there are three high ones, so I think that would pull it up more."

Then students work in pairs to try to find exactly where the mean should be by trying to equalize the distances of the data on each side of the mean. Remind them about the strategies they used in the last session to make the total distances on one side of the mean the same as the total distances on the

other side. Don't expect initial estimates to be accurate. When the distances are not identical, ask students which direction the mean should move and about how much it should move.

Students work on their constructions until they are satisfied about where the average is. Ask a couple of students to report to the whole group and explain how they made their construction.

If you wish, repeat this exercise with the second example on Student Sheet 5. This example may be harder because students must consider more data. Again, students can estimate, then gradually shift their estimate to find a balance point in the data.

In this discussion, or later in this session, students are likely to notice that the average is not always a value that actually appears in the data. Understanding that the average is a point of balance, not necessarily a value that is part of the data set, is the key to understanding what kind of "middle" the mean is. When the idea comes up, spend some time with your students discussing how the mean can give "real" information about the data even though it is not a "real" value in the data. See comments on this idea in the Teacher Note, *Is the mean a "real" number?* (page 46).

Considering the problem: What's the average amount of soda pop drunk by students in our class in a week?

Now we're going to figure out an average of how much soda pop the members of this class really drink. First, let's get some estimates. What do you think is the average number of cans or bottles drunk by people in this class during the last week?

Record students' estimates, and ask them about the reasons for their estimates. Then ask students about the relationship between their estimates and the shape of the data.

If Erica is right, and our average is around 7 or 8 cans, what would that mean? What are different situations that a mean of 7 or 8 might represent?

Students may come up with a variety of ideas, and you may want to ask some of the following questions if these points do not come up in the discussion:

What if everybody drinks the same amount of soda—what would our data look like?

What if most people drink about the same amount, but some drink a little less and some drink a little more?

What if a few people drink a lot of soda pop, a few drink none, and the rest are in the middle?

What if lots of students do not drink any soda pop and a lot of students drink it all the time?

Sketch some quick line plots on the board, or ask for volunteers to sketch different ideas about the shape of the data.

Examining our own data and finding the average

Students work in small groups of four or five members. They begin by making their own line plot on which they place the soda-pop data for their small group.

As a group, students should make estimates about where the average will be, and then use their own strategies to show where the average falls. They make adjustments in the average, as necessary, so the distances on one side of the average are the same as the distances on the other side. When they are sure of their average, they should draw a vertical line in pen at that value and write about the "proof" of their strategy. See the Teacher Note, *Finding the average of a small set of data* (page 47).

Putting it all together: Finding a class average

Put the data from the whole class on a line plot where everyone can see it.

Now that you have had some experience estimating the mean for a small amount of data, we can find the mean for the whole class. You are beginning to be able to look at a set of data and come up with a good estimate. By just looking at this line plot of all your data,

what would you say a good estimate would be for the average amount of soda pop drunk in a week by students in this class?

Allow time for students to give estimates, and make sure they give reasons for their estimates.

You've estimated that the mean will be somewhere between 6 and 8 cans of soda. Do you think you could find the exact mean for these data the way you did in your small groups?

Some students may feel confident that they could find the mean by estimating and adjusting, just as they did with only a few pieces of data. In fact, some students may even want to try this, and you may want to have them work on their own strategies first. Other students will point out that with so many pieces of data, it will be much more difficult to figure out how to balance distances. This is the place to introduce the algorithm for finding the mean.

Finding a short-cut: The formula for calculating the mean

☞ **WARNING:** Proceed with caution in teaching students how to use the algorithm! See the Teacher Note, *The limitations of learning the averaging algorithm* (page 49).

There are shortcuts to find the exact mean of a set of data—so you can tell what the number is where all the distances on one side exactly balance all the distances on the other side.

One of the shortcuts is something you've probably learned before. You add up all the data, and divide by the number of pieces of data. Let's try using this shortcut to find the average amount of soda pop drunk by members of this class.

Have students use their calculators to find the mean. Ask everyone for their findings. If there are discrepant findings, point out that it's easy to miscalculate when you use the algorithm because with real data there are usually a lot of different numbers to add up—and anyone can make mistakes adding up a long list of numbers. That's why it's essential to look at the data set and get an estimate of the mean before you calculate it. Sometimes an estimate may be all you need, and you may be able to get a good estimate by just looking at the data. At other times— for example, when you are comparing two sets of data—you may want to calculate the exact value of the mean.

Once a precise value for the mean has been found, close the discussion by comparing this result to the students' original estimates.

Is the class average higher or lower than you expected? What does the average tell us about the class data? What other characteristics of the data would be important to include in a description of soda-pop drinking by members of your class? Do you think these data are an accurate portrayal of the amount of soda pop your class drinks?

Students can also check their mean by looking at the whole set of data and estimating whether the sum of the distances on each side of the mean are equivalent. You may want to do this estimating as a whole class discussion while viewing the line plot of the class data.

Extension

Students may want to continue collecting data about soda pop drinking. They might collect their own data for another week and compare the two weeks. Or, they could collect data from another class or age group and compare the two groups. ∎

✎ TEACHER NOTE
Is the mean a "real" number?

Many students in the upper elementary grades are disturbed that the mean sometimes comes out to be a number that is not one of the values in the data set. For example, in the first set of data on Student Sheet 5, the average number of cans of soda drunk by the five students is 7, but they drank 0, 1, 10, 11, and 13 cans, respectively. No one drank 7 cans. Still, 7 does tell you something about the data: it is the point around which the data "balance," a kind of middle that takes into account all the values in the set.

An example that students often find absurd is one in which the mean is a decimal, but the actual data can only be whole numbers. In one class that had been collecting and analyzing data about family size, students figured out that the average family size in their class was 2.5 people. Some students claimed that this mean was "not real," protesting, "You can't have 0.5 of a child!" They decided that the mean did not give useful information because it was not a "realistic" value.

It is true that the mean is not "real" in the sense that the number of people in one of the families is "real." That is, if Sammy's family has 5 people in it, we can actually go out and touch and count the people. The 5 that Sammy records directly represents 5 of something in the real world.

An average is not "real" in this sense. It does not represent a particular thing that we can count in the physical world. But it is very real in a mathematical sense! It is a number that represents a real relationship among all the data. It summarizes *all* the family sizes and communicates that "on the average," students in this class have 2.5 people in their families. If the family size in our class is 2.5, but it's 3.5 in our penpal class, we know that our penpal class has somewhat larger families overall than we do.

Many values and expressions in mathematics, like averages, are "real" in a mathematical sense even if they cannot be counted or measured in the real world. For example, if 13 of the 25 students in your class take the bus to school, then about 1/2 or 50% of your students ride the bus. You can touch and count the 13 students, but you can't touch 1/2 or 50%. These numbers express *mathematical relationships*: about 1 out of every 2 students rides the bus; or, if you think of your class as having 100 students, then about 50 of those ride the bus.

Mathematics is a language that expresses relationships in the real world, even though many of its expressions, symbols, and values do not correspond to objects you can see and touch. In the primary grades, most of the mathematical values and symbols students encountered *did* correspond to objects and actions they could see, touch, count, and measure. But as students progress through

the upper elementary grades, they begin to encounter mathematics that is more abstract.

Talk with your students about how an average is a powerful mathematical tool that captures, in one number, a whole set of numbers so they can be described and compared. An average does not tell everything about a data set, but it can convey an important piece of information even though it does not seem entirely "real." ■

✏ TEACHER NOTE
Finding the average of a small set of data

Many students will enjoy the opportunity to prove that their average represents their data. Data sets should be kept small (about 6 pieces of data) so that this is a realistic task. Some sets should have an even number of values, others should have an odd number. This will help students see that it makes no difference how many data points are on either side of the mean: only the *total distance* of the data on either side of the mean has to be the same.

Here are two examples of the ways we have seen people prove and write about how their data set fits with a particular average. Students may have many ways of showing the fit; what is important is that they are able to prove how it works, and make use of the idea that the total distances of the data points from the mean are the same on both sides of the mean.

1. Making small jumps in to the mean.

One group of students considered the following soda-pop data from a line plot:

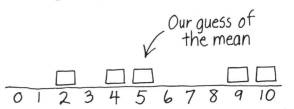

They estimated their mean to be about 5, explaining that "5 is the median and it's right between 0 and 10 so it's a good guess." Next, they decided to "jump the stick-ons in toward the mean." They did this as follows:

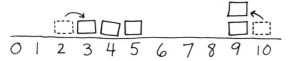

followed by:

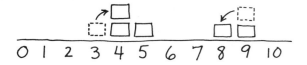

then by moving the outer data points in again to:

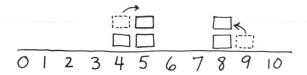

At this point, the students looked at their line plot and re-assessed the placement of the mean.

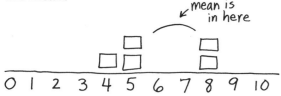

A student remarked "It couldn't be 5 because it really has to be somewhere between 5 and 8." They conjectured that the mean must be between 6 and 7, "but probably closer to 6 because there's a little more data lower down."

Using the same process of moving the stick-ons closer to the mean, in a one-for-one manner, the students soon arrived at this:

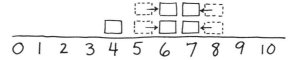

They then moved the 4 up to 6 (2 away), and both 7's down to 6 (a total of 2).

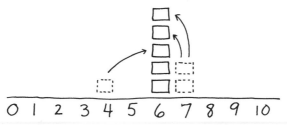

Their final mean was exactly 6, which surprised them. They wrote:

We were surprised it came out to exactly 6. We thought it would be closer to 6 and a half. Probably the 4 made a big difference in pulling it down lower.

2. Balancing total distances from the mean.

A second group of students had different data and a different approach. They made this diagram:

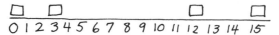

Then they wrote the following description:

Our data was 0, 3, 12, and 15 cans of soda. Julio isn't allowed to have soda, and Lisa drinks Coke all the time, even at breakfast. The rest of us thought that was gross. Anyway, our mean was a little less than 8, and here's how we can prove it. 8 is 8 away from 0 and 5 away from 3. That's 13. 8 is 4 away from 12 and 7 away from 15. That's 11.

13 on this side of . . .

            8

                    . . . 11 on this side.

So move the mean a little lower than 8 and it works!

In this data set, the actual mean is 7.5. Means frequently include decimals, but in this task students shouldn't worry about finding the precise decimal. It's fine for students to estimate the average as being a little above or below a whole number, or in the middle of two whole numbers. Estimating the average of a set of data is a skill students need to develop before they use the algorithm for finding the precise value of the mean.

Students may want to use the shortcut of adding up and dividing to get the average. Encourage them to hold off from doing this until they are reasonably confident that they have constructed an average that fits. Then, if they wish, they can use the algorithm to check their results. They learn about this "shortcut" at the end of the session on soda-pop drinking. ■

The limitations of learning the averaging algorithm

By the end of fourth grade, most students have learned that to find the average, you add up all the numbers and divide by the number of numbers. The trouble with this algorithm is that you do not have to understand anything about how the average represents the data set in order to use it. The significance of an average is that it helps you describe and summarize data. But many children focus only on the procedures of the algorithm and ignore the data entirely.

In research on children's understanding of average, we found that those who had learned only the algorithm got into trouble.* They picked a bunch of numbers, added them up, divided by some other number (frequently not the right one), and kept their fingers crossed. They believed in their answers—even if these answers were very unreasonable—because they thought they had applied the algorithm correctly.

For example, sixth grader Amy was asked to find the average weight of 10 people. Amy did not estimate a reasonable value for the result. Instead, she immediately applied the

*This research was carried out by Janice R. Mokros, Susan Jo Russell, Amy Shulman Weinberg, and Lynn Goldsmith under a grant from the National Science Foundation to Technical Education Research Centers.

algorithm—incorrectly—and got a mean of 790 pounds. Amy registered shock and disbelief at the 790 pounds. She knew the value was absurd, but rather than rejecting it, she slumped back in her chair and said, "I can live with that. I guess it's logical." "Logical?" asked the interviewer. Amy replied, "Yes, logical in that it's done the right way."

At least Amy was dismayed by the unreasonable number. All too many children found it quite easy to "live with" numbers that did not make sense because their calculation was done "the right way."

The algorithm is a simple shortcut. Encourage students to apply the algorithm only after they have sketched the data and estimated where the mean might be.

Whenever you can, help children build on their very reasonable, commonsense ideas about the average. Statements like these, which we have heard from fourth and sixth graders, should be encouraged:

▼ "At my store, soup costs 75 cents. But at the convenience store down the street they charge too much. It costs 98 cents there. I think the average might be somewhere between them, like maybe 85 cents."

▼ "Natural potato chips cost more. And health food brands. They bring up the

average amount. But chips on sale bring the average down."

▼ "If she ran an average of 5 miles a day, that doesn't mean she has to run the same amount every day. She might run a lot one day. On Saturday, she might have a date and not run at all!"

Once students have thought about how the data might go with an average, it is fine for them to check their ideas and estimates by using the algorithm. But this should be a late and relatively minor part of the data analysis process. And if students are having difficulty understanding how the mean represents the data, they are not ready to use the algorithm at all. The idea that a single number can somehow represent a whole set of numbers is a complex one. Students are far more likely to build an understanding of the relationship of the average to the data through a great deal of experience with a variety of data sets than by memorizing the procedure for finding the mean. ■

COMPARING SETS OF CEREAL DATA

INVESTIGATION OVERVIEW

What happens

Students use what they have learned to investigate a set of data about the sugar content of cereal. Then, using three data sets gathered at a supermarket, they investigate the hypothesis that cereals with higher sugar content are placed on the middle shelf of the store, where young children are most likely to see and select them. They analyze these data and prepare a report comparing the three sets.

The activities take two class sessions of about 45 minutes each.

What to plan ahead of time

▼ Prepare some activities to help students grasp what a gram is. Balance scales, gram weights, and a collection of common objects are the tools students need to gain some experience with weighing in grams. The science teacher in your school may have scales and weights (optional, before Session 1).

▼ Collect as many empty cereal boxes as possible so that each team or pair of students has 3–5 brands of cereal to look at. Try to collect a variety of cereal types, from those with no sugar to those with high sugar content (Session 1).

▼ Duplicate Student Sheet 6 (page 84) for each small group, or post this information where students can see it (Session 1).

▼ Duplicate Student Sheet 7 (page 85), for each small group (Session 1).

▼ Duplicate Students Sheets 8 and 9 (pages 86 and 87) for each small group (Session 2).

▼ Provide materials for students to draw and write about their comparison of the three data sets (Session 2).

▼ Have calculators available throughout the investigation.

Important mathematical ideas

Using middle values to compare data sets. Students use means and medians to describe and compare data. Averages like means and medians are useful because they convey information about the data they represent in an abbreviated form. Just as we sometimes want a brief summary of an event, rather than a blow-by-blow account, we often want an overall sense of the data without knowing every individual value. The usefulness of such summaries becomes especially apparent when we compare data sets. We do not want to say, "There are 6 cereals with 0 grams of sugar in Set A and 4 cereals with 0 grams in Set B; there are 4 cereals with 1 gram in Set A and 3 in Set B," and on and on. We would quickly lose our sense of the overall comparison. Capturing the data in a few numbers, such as the mean and the range, allows us to make overall comparisons. For example, "Set A had a mean value of 5 grams of sugar with a range from 0 to 14 grams, while Set B had a mean value of 9 grams of sugar and ranged from 4 to 15 grams."

Comparing the median and mean as summaries of the data. Sometimes the median and mean give similar information about a set of data. At other times they can be quite different. While the median gives the value that divides the data set in half, the mean measures where all the data "balance." By looking at the mean and the median in the context of the data, students can decide how well they think these measures describe the data as a whole or whether it is helpful to have both statistics.

Using the mean in the context of other information to describe a data set. The mean tells us something important about the relationship between the data and the balance point of the data. This information is especially useful for comparisons: Overall, one set of data has an average of 5 grams of sugar per serving while another set has 9.5 grams. The second set of data averages a greater sugar content than the first. However, the mean gives no information

about the shape of the data, their range, or where the clumps and holes might be. For example, we cannot tell from the mean whether all the data are grouped close to the mean or whether they are quite spread out. Some data sets may have the same mean, but quite different shapes (look, for example, at the supermarket data for the top shelf and bottom shelf of cereals, which have similar means but quite different overall profiles). ■

SESSION 1 ACTIVITIES

Getting ready: What's a gram of sugar? (Optional)

In this investigation students will be using data about the grams of sugar per serving in a variety of breakfast cereals. Students will be better able to understand and use these data if they have the chance to develop a feel for the weight of a gram. We suggest that students spend some time weighing common objects using a balance scale and a set of gram weights to get a sense of how much a gram is. Having some benchmarks in mind for grams is helpful. Here are a couple:

▼ A nickel weighs about 5 grams.

▼ A paper clip weighs about 1 gram.

Considering the problem: The sugar content of cereals

A lot of parents are concerned that from a very young age, their children are eating too much sugar. Some parents claim it's hard to keep sugary cereals away from their children because the supermarkets put them exactly where little people will be most tempted by them: on the middle shelf, which is just at children's eye level. Do you think these parents' claims are true?

Discuss students' own knowledge about sugary cereals and the ways supermarkets place these items so that they will sell.

Comparing cereals: What cereals are really sugary?

Distribute the empty cereal boxes you have been collecting so that each small group or pair of students has 3–5 different brands of cereal. Ask them to find the amount of sugar per serving listed in the nutritional information on the box and to compare that information with the list of sugar content in other foods, as provided on Student Sheet 6, *Sugar content of common foods*. After students have a chance to look at these data, ask them to report on what they found.

How does the sugar content of the cereals compare to the sugar content in other common foods? How do the cereals compare to each other?

Use this opportunity to discuss how the cereal companies define a "serving." Is the 1-ounce size that most cereals use as their definition a realistic serving?

Describing data: The cereals on the bottom shelf

We're going to look at three sets of data from a real supermarket. These data were collected at a supermarket in Massachusetts. One data set is the sugar content of cereals that were found on the highest shelf of the market, another is from those on the middle shelf, and the third is from those on the lowest shelf. You're going to work in teams to see if there were any differences among these three sets of data.

First we'll take a look at the bottom shelf cereal data together.

Hand out copies of Student Sheet 7, *Cereals on the bottom shelf*. The chart gives the number of grams of sugar per serving.

Working in pairs or groups of three, students organize these data. They might use a table or a line plot. Students find out and write down all they can about the cereals in this set of data. Each group of students jots down as many phrases as they can to describe these data ("lots of zeroes," "a lot more from 0 to 6 grams than in the higher numbers," "nothing at all from 7 to 9").

As you circulate, remind students to look at *all* the features of the data. If students calculate the mean, ask them whether they estimated first and whether the mean they calculated seems reasonable. What does it tell about the data? Some students might also look at the median. Encourage students to compare these two measures.

Bring the whole class together to discuss what they have found. A complete description of these cereals would include information about the shape of these data—where the data are clumped, what the range is, where there are no data—as well as information about the center of the data. Some students will have calculated the mean. If so, ask them to say something about what the mean communicates about the data. Others may have found the median. Why are these two measures somewhat different? What do they communicate about the data? See the Dialogue Box, *Cereals on the bottom shelf* (page 54). ■

66 99 DIALOGUE BOX
Cereals on the bottom shelf

LAUREN: We got a mean of 5.1.

And what did that tell you about the data?

ASHOK: That the average is 5.1.

Yes, the average is 5.1 grams. Did others of you get that? What does that statistic tell you?

ERICA: Well, we got 5.1 grams, too, so that seemed like 5.1 tells you about what you can expect to get on the bottom shelf—not real high sugar and not real low sugar.

SAMMY: Yeah, but that's not really true, because a lot of the cereals had no sugar at all.

JACOB: Six of the kinds of cereal had 0 grams.

So let's get some more description of these data and we'll come back to the mean in a minute. Jacob and Sammy noticed that an important feature of these data is that there are quite a lot of zeroes. What else did you notice?

MARTA: It's not just the zeroes, but there's a whole clump at the bottom.

CARL: If you count up all the 0s, 1s, 2s, and 3s, there are 13 kinds of cereal.

Can anyone say any more about this big clump?

PHIL: Yeah, that's 13 kinds of cereal at the lower end, and that's more than half of all of them.

What else?

MARTA: There's a few around 5 and 6.

JULIO: And a few around 10 and 11 and 13 and 14.

So what can you say about that?

ERICA: Well, there are a few real sugary ones on the bottom shelf, but really most of them are pretty low, from 0 to 6.

[*Later*] . . .

So, Lauren and Ashok were saying that the mean is 5.1 grams. Does that help you describe these data, if you were reporting about them to someone else?

SIRRAH: I don't think so. It's kind of misleading, because there's really not that many at 5 or around there.

JUANA: Yeah, but it's kind of in the middle. It does tell you it's kind of low, like Erica said before, from 0 to 6.

CAREN: But 5 isn't good, because that's really higher than a lot of them.

JUANA: But I still think it's like, well, there aren't only low ones. There's some high ones too, and that makes the average lean up toward the high ones a little.

PHIL: I want to say that our group found the median, and the median is 3 grams.

CAREN: And that seems more like it tells about where most of the data are. It's right in the middle of that whole big bunch.

So your group found out that the mean and the median are different? Why do you think they're different?

LAUREN: Because the median is the exact middle.

The median is the exact middle?

LAUREN: Yeah, and half of the cereals are from 0 to 3.

What do some of the rest of you think about what the mean and the median show about these data?

JACOB: I think you should use the median because 3 is really more around where most of them are.

BARBARA: Yeah, but you can't just ignore the 10s and 11s and all those. I think the mean is better, because it's not like you're always going to get low sugar on that shelf. There's some high ones too, and so you ought to know that the average is really a little higher than 3.

You've really noticed that in this case the mean and the median give slightly different information and you've come up with some interesting arguments about why you might rather know one than the other. If you only know that the median is 3, you do know that half of the cereal has 3 or fewer grams of sugar, but you don't know how high the other half might go. And if you just know that the

mean is 5, you do know that 5 grams is the overall average, but you don't have any idea how the data are spread out.

PHIL: Yeah, you should just look at the box of cereal, and that way you could tell for sure.

That's true, but supposing you wanted to report to parents or make some recommendations to supermarkets about what they do, then what numbers do you think it would be important for them to have? ■

SESSION 2 ACTIVITIES

Comparing the sugar data

Hand out copies of Student Sheets 8 and 9, the cereal data from the middle and top shelves of the supermarket, to each pair or small group of students.

In this session students will investigate the following question in their small groups: Is there higher sugar content in cereals on the middle shelf of this supermarket? Each group has five tasks:

1. Sketch the data from all three shelves.

2. Jot down phrases that describe each set of data (for example, "has lots of zeroes," "a huge clump between 11 and 13 grams," "nothing below 4 grams").

3. Estimate and then calculate the mean of each set.

4. Find the median of each set.

5. Decide how the three sets are similar or different.

Each group then writes a brief final report comparing the three sets of data, with illustrations. Encourage students to do rough drafts that include the phrases they have listed and sketches of each set. Then, when they have discussed what they found out, they can make a final draft with carefully drawn illustrations and a clear paragraph describing the similarities and differences. Do they think the claim is correct that cereals on the middle shelf contain more sugar? If there are differences in the three sets of data, are they really noticeable? How big would the differences have to be to convince parents that they were right?

Depending on the time available and whether or not students have reached closure in their small groups, you may want to end with a whole-class discussion, or make a class display of students' reports.

Extensions

There are many interesting comparisons to explore in the supermarket data. Here are some that your students may find interesting:

▼ On average, which companies produce brands that have the highest amount of sugar per serving?

▼ Identify what might be called the "health food" cereals. How does the average amount of sugar in these cereals compare to the overall average?

▼ Identify the children's cereals and the "adult" cereals. What's the average amount of sugar in these cereals? How much higher is one than the other?

Students can collect similar data from their own supermarkets and see if the findings are like the ones from New England. Their findings may be of interest to consumer groups or local parent-teacher associations.

Reporting on their results, either directly to these groups or by writing to the local newspaper, would be a valuable service to the community.

Every year the magazine *Consumer Reports* does a report on the nutritional content of cereal. They examine many variables, including sugar content, amount of protein, salt, and fat in a serving, and then rate the cereals. Their data would provide starting points for additional questions to study. Some students might be interested in devising their own rating system for evaluating the nutritional value of cereal. ■

MEANS IN THE NEWS

INVESTIGATION OVERVIEW

What happens

These sessions focus on interpreting real averages that we come across in the news or other sources. First, students consider the mean amount of ice cream eaten by a person in the United States annually (about 45 pints) and try to imagine how the data on which this average is based might actually look. Then, working in small groups, students select a real average from a provided list of statistics and write and illustrate a report on what this average tells about the data.

The activities take two class sessions of about 45 minutes each. The second session is largely devoted to students' group work on their reports.

What to plan ahead of time

▼ Collect examples of averages from the current news as well as situations in your school or community to supplement the statistics provided on Student Sheet 10. Students can participate in bringing in averages that they find (optional, before Session 1).

▼ Duplicate Student Sheet 10 (page 88), as well as any additional list of averages you have collected, for each student (Session 1).

▼ If you are planning to assess students' understanding of mean, this is a good point in the unit to do so. See the Extension at the end of the investigation (page 59).

Important mathematical ideas

Interpreting a given mean when we do not have access to the data. So far in this unit, students have been able to look at the whole set of data and see the relationship of the mean and the median to the rest of the data. As consumers of statistics, we are often confronted by average values—in the newspaper or other places—with no additional information. We might read that the average temperature this month was 81 degrees, that the median price for a single family home is $156,000, or that the mean number of traffic fatalities in our state is 12 each month. Understanding what the mean and median do and do not tell about the data is a key skill if students are to become responsible citizens who can use statistical information critically and carefully.

Using knowledge about a situation to help us interpret statistics. In order to interpret a mean, we need to know something about the data being described. When we come across an average in the news, how well we can interpret that statistic is related to how much we know about the situation it is describing. For example, if we read that the mean family size in our community is 3.2, we bring a great deal of knowledge about families to our understanding of this statistic. We know that none of the data can be 0, and that most of the data will be in the range of 1 to 6. We can easily imagine what the distribution of families might look like around a mean of 3.2. Interpreting the mean life expectancy in Ethiopia (39 years) is somewhat harder; what might the data look like? The more we know about the real situation being described, the easier it is to think about how the average might relate to the data.

Understanding that a statistic like the mean or median, by itself, is limited in the information it conveys. It is an unfortunate, but common, practice for newspapers and other information sources to report only the mean or median without any other information about the data. Averages are what statisticians call "measures of center." They give information about the middle or balance point of the data, but tell nothing about the spread of the data—how the data are distributed around the center or balance point, as discussed in the Teacher Note, *The mean stands alone* (page 60). ■

SESSION 1 AND 2 ACTIVITIES

Considering the problem: If we know an average, what do the data look like?

When we worked on the cereal problem and the family-size problem, we sometimes found out that a mean or a median can be the same for sets of data that look quite different. Do you remember any of those situations?

Discuss briefly what students remember about how an average could be the same for different sets of data.

Today we are going to look at some more real averages and think about what these averages *do* tell us and what they *don't* tell us. Often you'll come across averages—in the newspaper or in books when you're doing research on some topic—and you won't be able to see the data. You can only try to imagine what the data might actually look like. For example, here's one real average that was reported by Ben and Jerry's ice cream in 1990:

> **The average amount of ice cream eaten by a person in the United States is 45.14 pints per year.***

Ask students for their ideas about what this average means. What does the average tell us? What might the data have looked like? What can't we be sure about? As students

---

* *The Latest Scoop*, 1989 edition, Washington, DC: International Ice Cream Association.

talk, draw a couple of sketch graphs to go with their ideas, according to their directions, or ask students to come up and draw their own sketches. Because it's not possible to make an X for each person, these sketches will show only the overall shape of the graph—where it's high and where it's low. See the Dialogue Box, *Ice cream distributions* (page 60).

Students now work together in pairs or small groups for a short time to develop their own sketch of how they think the ice cream data might look for the whole population. Challenge the groups to come up with two sketches that look quite different, but both have an average of about 45 pints. It's fine for students to make sketches that have a mean of 45 pints, but are unrealistic and unlikely to occur in the real world; the process will help them understand what's possible.

Post students' sketches and discuss what kind of situation each one might represent. What would it tell about ice cream eating habits in the United States? Which ones are most likely to be close to reality? Which ones don't seem very likely?

Using experience to interpret a mean: What does it tell you? What doesn't it tell you?

You can see that just knowing the mean does not tell us exactly what the data are like, although it does give us a starting point for

imagining what the data could be. It's best if people give more information when they are reporting about their data, but in fact, many times the average is all that they report. However, if you know something about the topic, you can use your own experience to help you interpret what the average tells you about the data. For example, when we worked on family size, you all knew something about the size of families, so you could imagine what the data might look like. Today, you're going to use your own knowledge to help you interpret some real averages that were reported in newspapers and other sources.

Hand out Student Sheet 10, *Real means*, and any averages that you or the students have collected. Each pair or small group of students selects one average from the list and prepares a brief report about what that average tells them about the data. They should include several different graphs of how the data for this average might look, a brief description of each, and an explanation of which of these they think are more likely to be close to the real shape of the data. They may also comment on what information they feel is missing that would help them get a better picture of the data. What information did they wish they had? What would have been useful?

Emphasize to students that they use their own personal knowledge and experience to make a final graph that is as realistic as possible. You might also have students do some library research, especially for averages

on subjects that are less familiar to them. As you work with various groups, challenge them to justify their graphs.

Encourage students to make several sketches and to discuss and jot down their ideas first.

Students may need a second session to complete their work and report on it to the rest of the class. A final discussion might focus on what the mean does and does not communicate about the data and what other information would help give a better picture of the data set. See the Teacher Note, *The mean stands alone* (page 60).

Extension

Activities like the ones in this investigation are appropriate for assessing students' understanding of average. Bring in a few interesting averages from current magazines and newspapers. Ask students to choose one of the averages, draw the shape of the data that might go with it, and write a paragraph explaining what the graph shows. When evaluating a student's work, pay particular attention to (1) whether the average looks as if it is really "in the center of the data," either as the middle value (median) or as a balance point for the data (mean), and (2) how the student has explained the meaning of the graph. By this point in the unit, students should be able to link a provided average with a reasonable distribution of data. ■

What do you think that this average tells us?

ASHOK: Most people eat around 45 pints, but there's a lot on either side that eat either more or less than that.

I'm going to draw a sketch graph of what you're describing. Tell me how I should draw it.

ASHOK: Um, a big hump at 45 and then kind of tapering off.

OK, I'm not quite sure I know exactly, but let me try what I think you mean, and then we can change it. [*Sketches this line plot on the board.*]

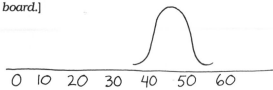

ASHOK: No, I think it would go out further, to like 30 and 60.

Like this? [*Draws the following.*]

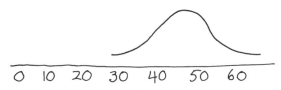

ASHOK: Yeah, that's good.

ERICA: I don't think that's realistic, because it doesn't include 0 or any really low numbers, and there are a lot of people who don't eat ice cream.

JACOB: Some are allergic.

SAMMY: Or babies might not be able to eat it, because their parents don't give it to them.

Who has an idea about how you would draw this differently?

MARTA: Start at 0 with a bunch of people, and then keep going across.

Why don't you show me what you mean?

[*Marta draws as follows:*]

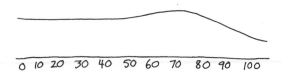

These two graphs look pretty different. Why did you do yours this way?

MARTA: Because I think that some people really eat a lot. And they have to balance out the babies and other people who eat zero.

What about the average in Marta's graph compared to Ashok's?

JACOB: They both look like they're about 45, but Ashok's is more squished.

LISA: Marta's got bigger distances from her average, but the distance on one side is still sort of the same as the distance on the other side. ■

By itself, the mean is not a complete description of any set of data. Although many popular sources of information do report only a mean—or median—to describe data, this is an unfortunate practice that is mathematically inappropriate. An average such as the mean or median only describes one characteristic of the data. It indicates where the data are centered. But this information about "center," as statisticians call it, is incomplete unless it is accompanied by a measure of "spread," that is, how the data are distributed around the center point.

Your students have already had some experience with the fact that the same mean or median can describe quite different distributions of data. For example, when they built different sets of data to represent an average family size of 4, they saw that, even with a small set of data, they could construct different data sets with the same mean.

The differences among data sets with the same average can be—although, of course, they are not always—dramatically different. For example, we know that the average amount of ice cream eaten by a person in the United States each year is about 45 pints. Can you picture what the shape of the data might actually be? What portion of the population eats around 40–50 pints? What portion eats a very small amount of ice

cream? What portion eats much more than 50 pints?

We know that the whole distribution of data balances at 45 pints, but there is a lot we do not know about the data. Given our own knowledge of ice cream, we might guess that there are some people who do not eat any—people on low cholesterol diets, for example. Babies probably would not eat ice cream (were children or only adults included when this statistic was determined?). On the other hand, it may be hard to figure out the highest possible amount of ice cream that someone might eat. Do some people eat 100 pints a year? 200 pints?

One piece of information that would have been helpful for interpreting this statistic is the range of the data: Is the range from 0 to 80, 0 to 150, 0 to 200? The range would help provide limits for us as we imagine how the data are spread out.

However, even though the range does provide helpful information, it still does not narrow down all the possible ways the data can be distributed around the mean. Perhaps most

people eat amounts of ice cream close to the average, with fewer people eating much more and much less, which would give us what is called a "normal" or "bell" curve in statistics, something like this:

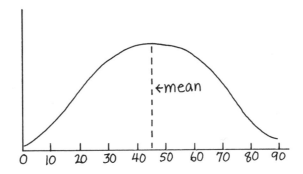

But this might not be true at all. Perhaps, in our more health-conscious society, there is a large group of people no longer eating ice cream, or eating lower amounts of ice cream, while there is also a sizeable group that eats a lot of ice cream, and not so many people in the middle. In that case, the distribution might look more like this:

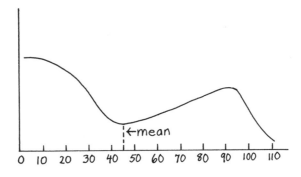

Finally, we could imagine a situation in

which many people are eating lower amounts of ice cream, but this large clump of people at the low end is balanced off by a long "tail" at the upper end, still giving an average of about 45 pints:

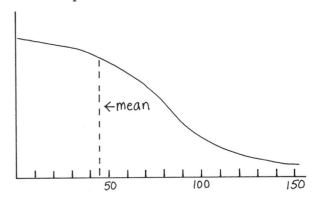

These three graphs represent very different situations in the world of ice cream eating, even though their means are the same. In describing the first, we would report that the mean is 45 pints, that people eat from 0 to 100 pints, and that about half of the data falls between about 30 and 60. In describing the second, we might say that, again, the mean is 45 pints, but that there are two prominent groups of people in the data: ice cream avoiders and ice cream gluttons.

In the third situation, while the mean is still 45 pints, we would want to add that the range goes from 0 to 150 and while there are a large number of people who eat relatively low amounts of ice cream with a steady drop-off as the number of pints increases, there is also a considerable clump of people spread out above the average who eat from 2 to 3 times the average amount of ice cream. We might want to report the median for this distribution. The median is about 40 and would tell us that about half the population is eating 40 or fewer pints of ice cream a year.

The mean and the median do provide some information, but these measures of center are most useful when they are accompanied by other descriptions of the range of the data and the way they are spread over that range.

We hope students will come to approach the use and interpretation of statistics according to the following guidelines:

1. When reporting on your own data, give a full, rich description of the data, including the mean or median, the range, and important characteristics of the spread of the data.

2. When interpreting data reported by others, try to obtain more information than the mean or median alone. If no other information is available, interpret a given average with caution, keeping in mind the different ways the data it represents could be distributed. ■

STATISTICS Middles, Means, and In-Betweens

PART 3

A project in data analysis

QUESTIONS ABOUT WORK

INVESTIGATION OVERVIEW

What happens

This more extended activity involves an investigation of the work people do, particularly around the home. The focus is on ways that students contribute to their households, as well as to the broader economy, through working.

In the first phase of this investigation (one or two sessions), students define what they mean by *work*. They examine the kinds and amount of work they do and the time they spend working. In the second phase (two or three sessions), they work independently in teams, either gathering similar data from another class (Option 1) or exploring in more depth their own attitudes toward work (Option 2).

The final project takes four or five class sessions, not including time for collecting

data from other classes. In the activity suggestions that follow, we have not broken the two general phases into specific sessions, because there is a lot of variation in what works for different classrooms in pacing a project like this.

What to plan ahead of time

▼ If your students will be collecting data from other classrooms (Option 1), make arrangements for them to visit those classes (Sessions 3–5).

▼ Be prepared to duplicate an "attitude survey" sheet that will be designed by the students, as described on page 74 (Option 2, Sessions 3–5).

▼ Provide materials for making and modifying rough draft graphs, including plain paper, squared paper, Unifix

cubes, counting materials, stick-on notes (Sessions 3–5).

▼ After the data have been collected, they will need to be compiled in one place where students have access to them. You might want to duplicate a list of everyone's data so each team can have a copy (Sessions 3–5).

▼ Provide materials for students to use in publishing their findings (Sessions 3–5).

▼ Have calculators available throughout the investigation.

Important mathematical ideas

Defining what is being investigated. The first phase in data analysis is defining the question and deciding what data are needed. Discussion is to be encouraged: What is meant by work? How do we determine how much time we spend working? In the first phase, students also decide how data are to be collected, and from whom.

Organizing, analyzing, and looking for patterns in the data. Students will organize their data to help with interpreting it and finding patterns. For example, a list of all the kinds of work done by sixth graders in a class is not as interesting or easy to interpret as a list that is also categorized by type of work (for example, Work at home, Volunteer work, Work for others for pay). Making decisions about outliers (do we count the "work" of the student who was on vacation during most of the data collection period?) is also part of this process. Data do not come pre-packaged; they need to be organized and categorized in a way that makes sense. Keep in mind that it is important for the students to make their own decisions about finding patterns in the data, even if their approach is different from one adults might take.

Building theories based on the data. Identifying patterns is the heart of the process of data analysis. Careful examination of data helps students learn to use evidence in answering their questions: How much time do young people typically spend working around the house? Are the jobs that sixth graders do much different from the jobs that fourth graders do? Throughout this investigation, students are encouraged to view the data from different perspectives, in order to address their own questions.

Using measures of "typicality" as ways of describing more complex data. Students use their entire repertoire of skills for describing the shape of the data, including various methods of looking at typicality. In comparing sets of data about amount of work, it is especially useful to use indicators of typicality, such as the median or mean, to summarize data. ■

SESSION 1 AND 2 ACTIVITIES

Investigating our own work

To introduce the topic of children and work, you may want to use some of the information in the Teacher Note, *Children and work* (page 71). If your students are reading any historical literature (for example, the Little House series by Laura Ingalls Wilder) or studying periods of history (for example, colonial America, the industrial revolution) in which children's work in a different time and place is described, such descriptions might be used to stimulate a discussion about children's work today. Emphasize work as a way that children make contributions to their homes and communities.

In our final project, you're going to be collecting data about the amount of work and the kinds of work that people your age do. What kinds of work are people your age usually expected to do? What does it mean "to do work"? What kinds of work do you do?

Give students an opportunity to explore what work means, particularly for themselves and others their age. They will be able to offer lots of personal examples of the work they do and may also have a lot of opinions about how much they like or dislike their work.

Defining the problem: What do we mean by "work"?

After students have had a chance to give

some examples of the kinds of work they do, focus the discussion on what they mean by "work." In order to collect data about work, students will need to create a definition of work. Allow for an extended discussion with time for controversy and disagreement as students try to formulate their own definition. For an example of the issues that may arise, see the Dialogue Box, *What is work?* (following).

There is, of course, no single correct definition. How your students define work will depend in part on what they are interested in finding out about themselves and other young people. You might use questions like these to prompt discussion:

If you were comparing the amount of time that you work with the amount of time your younger sisters and brothers work, what kinds of work would you want to include in the comparison? If we were going to compare this class with sixth graders in another school or another part of the country, what types of work would you want to know about? Would you include homework, or would it be more interesting to focus on chores and paid work?

❝❞DIALOGUE BOX
What is work?

What is work? What do you think of when I mention the word "work?"

JUANA: It's something you do because your parents tell you you have to do it.

MARTA: You get paid to do it—like babysitting or mowing the lawn.

SAMMY: I have to mow the lawn, but I don't get paid for it—and it's just as much work either way. So I don't think you have to be paid for it. Parents do a lot of work around the house, and they never get paid for it.

MARTA: But they should pay us if they ask us to do their work. Because it's their house.

JULIO: I don't get paid for washing dishes and helping out around the house.

MARTA: But you get an allowance, so that's kind of in return for the work.

JACOB: I have to do things like making my bed and taking out the trash. That's definitely work, and I don't get any allowance either.

ERICA: Work is stuff you do in school, too, like writing book reports or learning new spelling words.

JACOB: I don't think school work counts as work. Even though learning is sometimes hard work, I don't think that people usually think of "work" that way.

CAREN: And practicing the piano feels like work, but I wouldn't count that, because it's like getting to be good at something, and I really like it when I learn a new piece.

LISA: I agree with Jacob about learning. Like when I took swimming lessons, some of it was really hard, but it's still not the same thing as work.

Jacob and Lisa are saying that work is different from learning. Is there anything else that makes work different from other activities?

JULIO: It's something you do because you have to, not because you want to.

LISA: Not always! Sometimes you volunteer, like when we did the community clean-up on Earth Day.

SAMMY: Should we count homework?

What do people think?

ERICA: Let's count it because it's not really school and it's something you have to do.

Collecting data: What work do we do?

Once students are clear about what constitutes "work," help them generate a list of all the types of work they do, according to their definition. Encourage them to think about all the different ways they are involved in doing work. As they make their list, further clarification of their definition may be needed;

Babysitting	X X X X X X X X
Dishwashing	X X X X X X X X
Lawn mowing	X X X X
Trash out	X X X X X X X
Snow shoveling	X X X X X X X X
Pet care	X X X X X X X X X X X X
Plant watering	X X X X X
School assistant	X X X X X X X X X X X X X
Clean own room	X X X X X X X X X X X X
Bed making	X X X X X
Make earrings	X X X X
Leaf raking	X X X X X X X
Dog walking	X X X X
Garage cleaning	X
Do laundry	X X X X X X X X
Yard clean-up	X X X X
Vacuuming	X X X X X X X
Set table	X X X X X X X X X
Sweeping floor	X X X X
Newspaper delivery	X X X
Help with cooking	X X X X X X X X X
Clean/clear table	X X X X X X X X X
Empty dishwasher	X X X X
Dust house	X X X X
Rearrange furniture	X X X X X
Gardening	X X X X X X

for example, "We said we would not include homework, but what about when I help my little sister do her homework?" Students will also need to make decisions about categories: Are washing the dishes and emptying the dishwasher two different jobs?

Keep in mind that there may be some sensitive issues in this discussion and subsequent ones. See the Teacher Note, *Dealing with sensitive work issues* (page 72).

We're going to take a quick survey of how many of you do the different kinds of work we have identified. How should we do this?

Students will probably suggest that you do a "show of hands" and make a tally or write numbers beside each task in the list you made earlier. One class developed the list shown at left.

Describing the data: A first look at the work we do

What would you say about our data? What kinds of work are typical for our class?

Students may want to comment about individual activities. After some discussion, ask students about patterns that they notice in the data. What types of tasks are most common among their group? What types of tasks are done by only a few people? The Dialogue Box, *Looking for patterns in our work data* (following), provides an example of students collaborating to analyze the work data collected to this point in the activity.

❝❞DIALOGUE BOX
Looking for patterns in our work data

What do you notice in our list of jobs?

SAMMY: There sure are a lot of us that have to clean our rooms!

JULIO: And do pet care, and be school assistants.

ERICA: That's because everybody has to be a school assistant sometime during the year.

MARTA: It seems like not many people do messy jobs like garage cleaning and yard clean-up.

Messy jobs?

MARTA: Yeah, jobs where you get dirty.

So using your definition, let's look through the list and see if we can find a pattern. Are people in this class less likely to do messy jobs than other jobs?

JACOB: I don't think that's true, because one-third of us take the trash out, which is really messy.

JUANA: Exactly what jobs go into this category?

JULIO: I'd say lawn, trash, leaf raking, garage cleaning, yard clean-up, and gardening.

SAMMY: Hey, those are all outside jobs, not just messy jobs. Maybe we don't do outside jobs as much as inside jobs.

CAREN: It is true that most of the really popular jobs are inside jobs. Although it's hard to tell with "pet care," because it's outside if you're walking your dog, but it's inside if you're feeding her or brushing her.

LISA: But we decided that pet care is a different job from dog walking, so pet care is an inside job.

MARTA: I think we do more jobs inside, because if you just count up the number of inside jobs that 5 or more of us do, there's a lot: Babysitting, dishwashing, plant watering, school assistant, cleaning our rooms, pet care, making beds, doing laundry, vacuuming, setting the table, cooking, clearing the table, rearranging furniture. Let's see . . . that's 13 inside jobs that 5 or more of us do.

How does that compare to the outside jobs?

☛ In this discussion, children are beginning to sort the jobs into larger categories in their attempts to say something more general about the findings. Students may use many different strategies for looking at the big picture, and many of these strategies will involve forming categories of jobs. Students need to work out their own methods for categorizing and looking at patterns, even if their methods may not be as neat and tidy as yours. Struggling with messy data is what data analysis is all about.

Collecting more data: How much time do we spend working?

Now we're going to determine how much time each of you typically spends doing the work you have identified.

Give students an opportunity to discuss how they can determine how much time they spend doing each type of task. They need to be clear about the time frame they are using. Should it be for just a day? Should they just look at yesterday? Do they want to pick their "heaviest" work day—for example, Saturday when they are home—and see how much time they spend working? Should they try to describe a typical week? What about seasonal types of work, such as snow shoveling—how will these be counted?

One class decided that they would try to describe a typical week, especially since many of their tasks occurred weekly, not daily. They also decided to "prorate" their seasonal work by figuring out how many weeks they had to do work like gardening or snow shoveling, how much time they spent on it each week, and then how much time this would be each week if they spread it out through the whole year. In other words, they found the average amount of time spent gardening every week, even though there were many weeks in the year when there was no time spent on this job.

Once students have a strategy for determining "time spent working," give them an opportunity to work together in groups of three or four to determine the amount of work each person does. One strategy students have found useful is to determine the amount of work spent on each task on their list during the specified period of time, then get a total. Students can work collaboratively on the difficult calculation problems that are likely to arise in this activity.

Recording and describing the data:
What is the typical amount of time
we work?

After the data have been collected, display the data. For example, one group of twelve students made a graph like the one shown at the right.

They could also have grouped the data and displayed them on a line plot like this:

```
      X
      X X           X
X   X X X X X           X
0 1 2 3 4 5 6 7 8 9 10 11 12 13 14 15 16 17 18 19 20
```

What would you say about our data? What is the typical amount of time people in our class spend working in a week?

Students describe the shape of the data as well as what is typical in the data. They may want to examine the mean or median amount of time spent on work. Perhaps their data has some unusual values. For example, in the data from the class above, students first determined the mean for the whole class, which was 6 hours a week. Then they decided not to include Marta's data, and they found that the mean had changed to 4.5 hours a week. They were exploring the effects of Marta's very large number of hours of work as compared with what seemed typical for the rest of the class members. ■

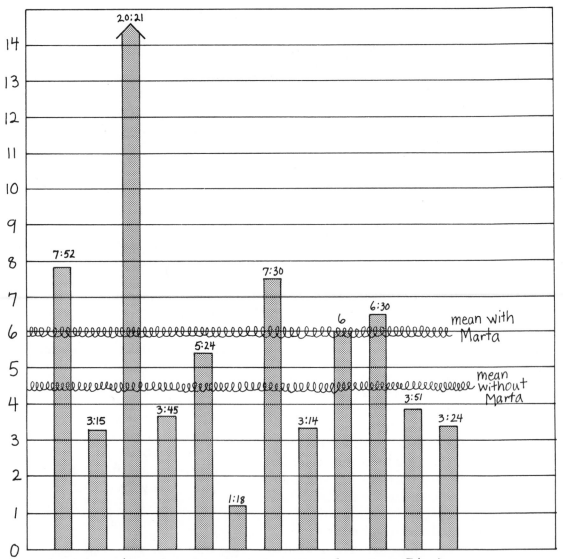

The focus of this project is on the positive contributions children make to their homes and community through all kinds of work. Educators and others who study young people's work appear to agree that when students make contributions to their families and communities, such work helps them develop a sense of responsibility and also helps them understand the value of their educational experience in the real world. Studies of high school students indicate that those who work at a part-time job a few hours a week had higher grades than students who did not work, although students who worked long hours had very low grades.

Much of what your students will talk about will be work within their own families—chores they are expected to do, or jobs they do to earn their allowance. Some of your students may also do "real" work, such as farm work or helping parents who are self-employed with paid work they do at home.

Because of the abuses of child labor in factories and on farms in the early history of our country, a series of child labor laws have been passed in the United States.* These laws restrict the amount and types of work school-aged children can legally do. For

* The information about child labor laws in this Teacher Note is from articles in *The Boston Globe*, 4/22/90 and 4/24/90.

example, federal child labor laws restrict 14- and 15-year-olds to 3 hours a day, 15 hours a week of work during school periods and 8 hours a day, 40 hours a week when school is not in session. They are also prohibited from working before 7 a.m. and after 7 p.m. during the school year but can work until 9 p.m. during the summer. The types of work students can do at this age are also very carefully defined.

When students turn 16 years old, there are no longer any restrictions on the amount of work they can do, although 16- and 17-year-olds are still prohibited from working with hazardous equipment and from driving for commercial purposes. Your students may want to share their knowledge about the kinds of work their older siblings do. Since there are many thousands of violations of child labor laws, do not be surprised if your students bring up incidents from their own experience in which these laws have been violated.

There are exceptions to the general age limits for children working outside the home. For example, children can work on farms as young as age 12 (with restrictions about work during school hours and work on hazardous equipment).

Another exception that has been written into federal law for 50 years involves newspaper carriers. Different states have different regulations about age limits for newspaper carriers. Recently in Massachusetts, the

minimum age was lowered from 12 to 9. This change caused a great deal of controversy. One state legislator, whose 8-year-old daughter lost her job of delivering 9 newspapers, fought for lowering the age limit, as did the Massachusetts Newspaper Publishers Association. However, some child advocacy groups were concerned about children as young as 9 years old delivering newspapers.

Since your students are nearing the age when they can work outside the home at paid jobs, they may be interested in the regulations in your state. They may be interested in the newspaper carrier controversy, or the pros and cons of children engaged in farm work. ■

✎ TEACHER NOTE
Dealing with sensitive work issues

Collecting and discussing data about work, like much of the other data that is really interesting to students, may touch on sensitive areas for some of your students. Some students in your class may need to spend a good deal of time working in order to help out with family finances. For some such students, their work may be a matter of embarrassment rather than pride. Perhaps the work they do keeps them from having friends or participating in activities with other children their age. Some students may even be involved in work that is prohibited for their age group and thus may be unwilling to talk about it.

Depending on your own teaching style and approach, you might use this investigation as an opportunity to make such students feel more included and accepted. Let them know that their opinions about work are interesting and valuable, that they have good experience and knowledge to contribute to this study. Some students may not want to volunteer information about particular aspects of their work, and of course their choice should be respected. Teachers can handle potentially sensitive data by having students initially contribute their data anonymously. Students write down their information, and then the teacher compiles it

on a list without indicating students' names. Usually, as the study proceeds, students find that there are many similarities between themselves and others. As they become interested in the questions and issues that arise, they become much more comfortable about sharing information they were initially reluctant to discuss. ■

SESSION 3– 5 ACTIVITIES

Independent project investigations

For the remainder of this investigation, students work on small teams to pursue one of two activities to extend their initial work:

▼ **Option 1: Investigating work done by another class.** Students identify a comparison class in the same or a different grade. Using their list of work tasks, they survey this other class to find who does what work, and to identify the amount of "time spent working" using their definition. They find ways to display and compare these new data with their own data about work.

▼ **Option 2: Investigating attitudes toward work**. Students explore their attitudes toward the tasks they have identified as work. As part of this activity, they become familiar with developing an attitude scale. Then they identify typical attitudes and discuss what this tells them overall about how they feel about work.

While it is easier to organize this investigation if all teams are working on the same option, you may choose to let some work on Option 1 and others on Option 2. What you decide will depend in part on how much experience your students have had working cooperatively in independent small groups.

Whichever option students choose, the

nature of their work will be similar. They will collect data, organize and represent them, describe and summarize them, and finally interpret their findings. Encourage students to make rough draft graphs so they can see the general shape of their data. Remind them that they need time to work with their data and look for patterns before they become concerned with making graphs that are neat, colorful, and carefully labelled.

Similarly, guide students to jot down the ideas they have as they look at their data ("average about the same as for our class," "fewer kids in the middle, right around the average," "nobody does babysitting in their class"). Help students remember that the mean or the median gives them only partial information about their data. The average is an important statistic, but is more meaningful if it is part of a broader description of the important features of the data. See the Teacher Note, *The mean stands alone* (page 60).

Only when student teams have looked carefully at their data and have decided what to say about them are they ready to publish their results. For more information, see the Teacher Note, *Phases of data analysis: Learning from the process approach to writing* (page 75). At that point they will be ready to make final drafts of their graphs and write a final report about their findings. Final reports should include:

▼ a description of how and from whom they collected their data

▼ any problems they ran across in the data collection process

▼ a description of their data, including important features of the data and summary statistics, such as the mean, median, and range

▼ their interpretation of the data, including comments on what they found when they compared sets of data

▼ theories about their interpretation; what accounts for the differences (or similarities) they found?

▼ illustrations of their findings, including appropriate graphs

Students can divide up these tasks among their team members. Each member does a rough draft of his or her part of the report, then shares it with the rest of the team, who critique it before final drafts are written. You may want to meet with each team for a feedback session on the rough drafts of their work.

In some classes, each team reports back on their work to the whole class. In others, teachers make arrangements for the students to report to another class, to parents, or to the principal. Since students will have put a great deal of work into their written report, they may prefer not to report on it orally as well. You might make a display of the final reports, then conclude with a class discussion about the process of data

analysis: What were the problems students ran into? What were the most interesting findings? What are new questions they have now? What would they do differently next time?

Following are guidelines for proceeding with the two options.

Option 1: Investigating work done by another class

Are other classes like ours in terms of the kinds and amount of work that they do? How might work be different for students who are a little younger or a little older? Would the amount and type of work look the same for another class in the same grade in our school?

There are many questions of interest here. Some classes might be particularly interested in looking at the work of older students—in order to get a glimpse of what's in store for them! Others might want to compare themselves with another class from the same grade. And still others want to compare themselves with students from lower grades—to see how far they've come.

Students discuss the possible comparisons and choose the one that is of most interest. They decide how they will accomplish the data gathering. Then they take the survey they developed to members of the other class and ask them to indicate which work activities they do, as well as the total amount of time they spend working (in the specified time period).

As part of collecting these data, students will need to do the following:

1. Devise a method for collecting and recording their data.

2. Make sure they can explain to someone else exactly what they mean by each task mentioned in the survey.

3. Be able to help other students count the amount of time they spend on each task.

Students also need to make plans for introducing their survey to the other class. Will one team go into the other class and present the survey, asking each class member to fill out information on a survey form? Or, will team members work individually with students from the other class to get the information? Or, will survey forms be given to the other class's teacher to hand out to the students?

After the data are gathered, students work in small groups of three of four to organize and analyze the new data and to compare them to the data from their own class. The data will need to be listed and duplicated so that each small group has a copy of all the data. Student teams will also need access to a copy of the data from their own class.

Encourage students to draw graphs that show both sets of data so their similarities and differences can be seen easily. Reports can focus on such questions as: What

patterns did we see in the other class? How are they like or unlike our class? Are there any surprises? What might account for the differences?

Option 2: Investigating attitudes toward work

Sometimes people have strong feelings about the work they do. They may really like their work. For example, you may like to take your dog for a walk because it gets you outside, and it gives you time to play with your dog. Other kinds of work may not be so popular. Perhaps you really do not like to clean your room or make your bed, but you do it because you are expected to. You probably have different attitudes toward different types of work.

In an initial discussion to start off this investigation, students can share some of their "pet peeves" as well as the things they like to do. After some discussion, ask students:

How do you suppose we might gather data about people's attitudes toward their different work activities?

Discuss various ways students might examine their own opinions about the jobs they have listed. Help them explore ways of using numbers to record attitudes, introducing the idea of a scale for measuring attitudes, as described in the Teacher Note, *Measuring things that don't come in numbers* (page 76).

Students will design their own attitude survey sheet. They need to decide on their rating scale, and they may want to select a subset of the work tasks they have identified. We suggest that you choose tasks from the list with which the majority of the students have had some experience. This will allow more students to contribute their attitudes about tasks they actually do.

Once the attitude survey sheet is complete, make enough copies so that everyone in the class can have one to fill out. Talk with the students about trying to get accurate data. Perhaps students should fill out the forms privately and anonymously, so that each student is making independent decisions.

Once the data have been gathered, break the students into working teams. One way to distribute the analysis work is to divide the items from the survey among the teams. For example, if there were 15 items on the data survey and there are five teams of students, the first team can take all the data from items 1–3, the second team all the data from items 4–6, and so forth. However, don't worry if this division doesn't work perfectly; it doesn't matter if some students work with the same data. In fact, it is interesting to see if students analyzing the same data notice different things and come up with different theories.

Students work in their small groups to organize and analyze the data. They will describe the data for each of the tasks (walking the dog, taking out the garbage) and identify the typical attitude by finding the mean and/or median rating given to that task. Remind students that when thinking about typical, they should exclude the "not applicable" ratings. They will be looking only at the people who have given ratings to the task.

Students' final reports on their data can focus on such questions as: What can we say about our attitudes toward work? Are there any surprises? Do you have any theories about the kinds of work people like to do? About the kinds of work they would rather *not* do? ■

✎ TEACHER NOTE
Phases of data analysis: Learning from the process approach to writing

The process of data analysis is similar to many other creative processes. Students doing data analysis follow the same processes that adults do; the analyses may be less complex, but the procedures are the same. In data analysis, as in writing or art, teachers help children do real work rather than stilted school assignments requiring fill-in-the-blank responses. The teacher's role is relatively subtle—shaping the process, asking questions that guide the students' progress toward their goals, hearing and responding to their ideas and theories. Students are expected to have something original and interesting to say, and the teacher provides an environment that enriches and supports students' self-expression.

Data analysis has many similarities to the process approach to writing, which typically includes four phases. The process starts with a *planning phase* (often called pre-writing or brainstorming). This is followed by the *writing phase*, when a very rough draft of ideas is first put down on paper. The third phase is the *revision* or *rewriting phase* when the writer elaborates, clarifies, restructures, and edits the piece. The final phase is the *publication phase*, when the writer's

completed piece is shared with others. These processes may be reiterated until the piece of writing is finished.

Data analysis has four phases parallel to those in the writing process:

Phase One: Brainstorming and planning. During this time, students discuss, debate, and think about their research question. In some cases, defining and agreeing upon the question may take a considerable amount of time. Having defined the question and agreed upon terms, students consider possible sources of data, ways of recording them, and how they might organize themselves to collect needed information.

Phase Two: Putting it on paper. Collection and representation of data allows students to develop their "discovery drafts"—what we call "sketch graphs"—the first draft of the information on which they base their developing theories. Students represent the data in a variety of ways to help them describe the important features. They use their first drafts as tools as they look for relationships and patterns in the data.

Phase Three: Revision. Writers are encouraged to share their drafts with their peers in order to determine how an audience perceives their work. Similarly, in the data analysis process, the students often present their sketch graphs, preliminary findings, and beginning theories to their working group in order to see whether their interpretations seem supported by the data, and whether others see things they haven't noticed. Revision in data analysis may include finding new ways to organize and represent the data, developing better descriptions of the data, collecting additional data, or refining the research questions and collecting a different kind of data.

Phase Four: Publication or display. The nature of "publishing" the results of data analysis varies, just as it does for a story or essay. Sometimes students develop a theory that is the basis for a report on a particular topic; at other times they may develop a theory that inspires further investigation. A completed report of a data analysis investigation may involve a written description of the study with conclusions and recommendations, final presentation graphs of information previously displayed in working graphs, and a verbal or written presentation of the report to an interested audience.

When teachers think about the writing process, their role as facilitator and helper seems familiar and obvious. Of course students need time to think and revise their work! Of course they need to be challenged and led, sensitively, to the next level of awareness. The writing process seems more familiar to most of us than the mathematics process because we, too, have done writing.

The process of data analysis needs the same kind of teacher support. Students need to try their ideas, to rough them out, to be challenged and encouraged to go further in their thinking. It is important that they have time to think and to consider options—and vitally important that they see their work as part of a process. Data analysis, like writing, is not cut and dried. There are many ways to approach a question and many conclusions to be drawn. Like writing, mathematical investigation is a creative blend of precision and imagination. ■

✎ TEACHER NOTE
Measuring things that don't come in numbers

One way researchers collect data on things that cannot be counted or measured directly is to make a scale of numbers. For example, an attitude survey toward work children do could be set up like this:

	Dislike a lot			Like a lot		
Compared to all the work you do, how much do you like to do each activity listed below? A rating of 1 means you really *don't* like to do it, and 5 means you really *do* like to do it. Of course, if you don't ever do this task, you would circle the phrase "I don't do this" instead of a number.						
walk the dog	1	2	3	4	5	I don't do this
make my bed	1	2	3	4	5	I don't do this
do the dishes	1	2	3	4	5	I don't do this
clean the yard	1	2	3	4	5	I don't do this

From the instructions, it should be clear to students that if a person circles a 1, it means he or she really does *not* like this task; if a 5 is circled, that task is a favorite. You might ask students to explain what a 2 means, or a 3, or a 4.

In this investigation, students will need to design a similar data gathering sheet that lists the tasks on the left and the rating scale on the right. They can decide how many numbers there should be (1–3? 1–5? 1–10?). They can also decide whether they want to label each number on the scale (1 = like it a lot; 2 = like it some, 3 = don't care one way or the other, and so forth) and which direction the scale goes. (Does a 1 mean "I love it" or "I hate it?")

It is important to have some option for people who don't have any opinion because they never do that kind of work. The "I don't do this" category is one solution; another option is to have them leave that item blank.

Students need to make many decisions as they design their attitude surveys. Encourage them to take the time to think carefully about these decisions, because better-designed surveys yield data that are easier to analyze. ■

SAMPLES OF RAISIN DATA

SCHOOL A

```
            X  X
            X  X  X  X
            X  X  X  X  X  X  X  X
            X  X  X  X  X  X  X  X  X  X
            X  X  X  X  X  X  X  X  X  X
      X              X  X  X  X  X  X  X  X              X
24 25 26 27 28 29 30 31 32 33 34 35 36 37 38 39 40 41 42 43 44
```

SCHOOL B

```
                  X
                  X  X
                  X  X  X        X  X  X  X
            X     X  X  X  X  X  X  X  X  X
            X  X  X  X  X  X  X  X  X  X  X
      X  X  X  X  X  X  X  X  X  X  X  X
   X  X  X  X  X  X  X  X  X  X  X  X
24 25 26 27 28 29 30 31 32 33 34 35 36 37 38 39 40 41 42 43 44
```

PULSE RATES FOR TWO AGE GROUPS

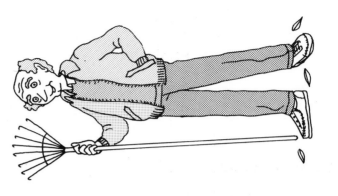

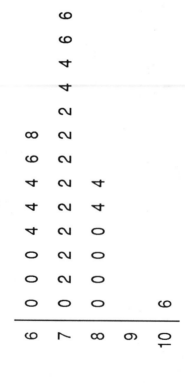

```
12 | 0 8
13 | 4 6 6
14 | 0 0 0 0 0 2 4 6
15 | 0 2 4 6 6 6 6
16 | 0 0 0 0 0 0
```

Pulse rates of newborn infants

```
 6 | 0 0 0 4 4 6 8
 7 | 0 2 2 2 2 2 2 4 6 6 8
 8 | 0 0 0 0 4 4
 9 |
10 | 6
```

Pulse rates of people 60–65 years old

ANIMAL PULSE RATES

Stem	Leaves	Animals
1	6	Whale
2	5 9	Camel, Shark
3	0 5 5 7 8 8	Elephant, Horse, Trout, Haddock, Salmon, Goldfish
4	0 0 2 4 7 8 8	Mule, Donkey, Lion, Seal, Alligator, Crocodile, Cod, Frog
5	5 5 9	Cow, Bear, Carp, Perch
6	6	Giraffe
7	0 0 0 5	Human, Deer, Ostrich, Pig, Sheep
8	0 0 0	Goat, Groundhog
9	0 2 5	Pointer, Basset hound, Fox terrier
10	0 0	Collie, Irish terrier
11	0	Dolphin
12	0 0 5 8	Kangaroo, Beagle, Boston terrier, Pekingese, Bass
13	0	Cat
14	0	Beaver
15	0	Rabbit
16		
17	0	Pigeon
18		
19		
20		
21	1	Turkey
22		
23		
24	0	Fox
25		
26	8	Duck
27	0	Guinea pig
28		
29		
30	0 1	Porcupine, Buzzard
31	2	Quail
32	0	Chicken
33		
34	0 2 7 7	Mink, Falcon, Goshawk, Hawk
35	0	Chipmunk
36		
37	8	Crow
38	0 8	Rook, Weasel
39	0	Squirrel
40	1	Gull
41		
·		
·		
58	8	Bat
59		
60	0	Mouse

RECORD SHEET FOR PAPER CLIP SCORES

Group _____

Player's name	Trial no.	Score (distance)	Comments

Statistics: Middles, Means, and In-Betweens

WHAT'S THE AVERAGE?

Here are data from five students showing the
amount of soda pop they drank during one week.

```
X X                       X  X    X
0  1  2  3  4  5  6  7  8  9  10 11 12 13 14 15
```

Eight students in a sixth grade class kept track
of how much soda pop they drank in a week.
Here is the graph of their data.

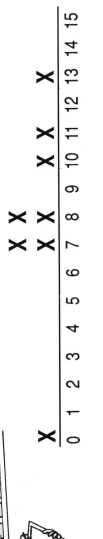

```
                  X  X
                  X  X     X  X  X     X
X
0  1  2  3  4  5  6  7  8  9  10 11 12 13 14 15
```

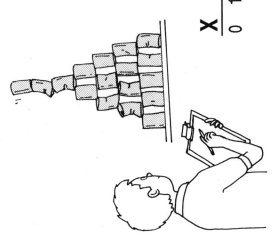

SUGAR CONTENT OF COMMON FOODS

Food	Portion (or serving)	Total sugar (grams)
American cheese	1 slice	2.1
Apple (raw)	1 medium	15.7
Bacon	2 slices	0.0
Banana (raw)	1 average	22.4
Blueberry muffin	1 average	5.7
Carrot (raw)	1 medium	4.8
Catsup	1 tbsp.	3.4
Chocolate candy bar (plain)	1 oz.	14.5
Cola	12 oz.	37.4
Cranberry juice cocktail	4 oz.	21.0
Creamsicle (orange)	1	16.4
Grapefruit (raw)	1/2 average	4.9
Grapes (green, seedless)	1/2 cup	13.1
Hi-C apple drink	8 oz.	30.5
Honey	1 tbsp.	17.3
Hostess devil's food cupcake	1 cake	14.2
Ice cream, Baskin Robbins strawberry	2/3 cup	29.9
Ice cream, Baskin Robbins vanilla	2/3 cup	18.4
Milk (whole)	8 oz.	11.4
Orange (raw)	1 medium	12.1
Peanut butter	1 tbsp.	.1
Pickle (dill, whole)	1 medium	1.8
Pudding (Jello instant chocolate w/ whole milk)	1/2 cup	27.0
Raisins	1/4 cup	26.9
7-Up	12 oz.	36.5
Snickers	1 oz. bar	13.3
Sugar (brown)	1 cup	216.0
Sugar (granulated)	1 cup	199.0
Sugar (white)	1 cube	7.0
Yogurt (lowfat, fruit)	1 cup	43.2

From: G.A. Levielle, M.E. Zabik, and K.J. Morgan, *Nutrients in Foods* (Cambridge, MA: The Nutrition Guild, 1983).

CEREALS ON THE BOTTOM SHELF

Cereal	Sugar	Brand
Super Golden Crisp	14	Post
Honey Comb	14	Post
Alphabits	11	Post
Alphabits (marshmallow)	13	Post
Shredded Wheat	0	Sunshine
Shredded Wheat (bite size)	0	Sunshine
100% Bran	6	Nabisco
Shredded wheat	0	Nabisco
Team Flakes	5	Nabisco
Shredded Wheat (spoon size)	0	Nabisco
Cheerios	1	General Mills
Cheerios (apple cinnamon)	10	General Mills
Cheerios (nut and honey)	10	General Mills
Total	2	General Mills
Wheaties	3	General Mills
Product 19	3	Kellogg's
Rice Krispies	3	Kellogg's
Special K	3	Kellogg's
Frosted Flakes	11	Kellogg's
Corn Flakes	2	Kellogg's
Crunchy Bran	6	Quaker
Life	5	Quaker
Life (cinnamon)	6	Quaker
Puffed Wheat	0	Quaker
Puffed Rice	0	Quaker

CEREALS ON THE MIDDLE SHELF

Cereal	Sugar	Brand
Raisin Bran	5	Post
Fruity Pebbles	12	Post
Cocoa Pebbles	13	Post
Honey Bunches of Oats	6	Post
Breakfast Bears (cinnamon)	7	Nabisco
Breakfast Bears (chocolate)	7	Nabisco
Breakfast Bears (honey)	7	Nabisco
Almond Delight	8	Ralston
Batman	10	Ralston
Hot Wheels	11	Ralston
Cookie Crisp (chocolate chip)	13	Ralston
Clusters	7	General Mills
Raisin Nut Bran	8	General Mills
Trix	12	General Mills
Oatmeal Crisp	6	General Mills
Golden Grahams	9	General Mills
Cocoa Puffs	9	General Mills
Cinnamon Toast Crunch	11	General Mills
Lucky Charms	11	General Mills
Count Chocula	13	General Mills
Honey Smacks	15	Kellogg's
Cocoa Krispies	11	Kellogg's
Fruitful Bran	11	Kellogg's
Frosted Mini Wheats	6	Kellogg's
Frosted Mini Wheats (bite size)	7	Kellogg's
Nut and Honey Crunch	9	Kellogg's
Just Right	9	Kellogg's
Shredded Wheat (apple cinnamon)	6	Kellogg's
Shredded Wheat (raisin)	6	Kellogg's
Raisin Bran	13	Kellogg's
Apple Jacks	14	Kellogg's
Corn Pops	12	Kellogg's
Fruit Loops	13	Kellogg's
Oh's (honey graham)	11	Quaker
Cap'n Crunch	12	Quaker
Cap'n Crunch (peanut butter)	10	Quaker
Cap'n Crunch (crunch berries)	12	Quaker
Rice Bran	6	Quaker
Oat Bran	4	Quaker

Statistics: Middles, Means, and In-Betweens

CEREALS ON THE TOP SHELF

Cereal	Sugar	Brand
Grape Nuts	3	Post
Grape Nuts Flakes	5	Post
Raisin Grape Nuts	6	Post
Bran Flakes	5	Post
Fruit and Fiber	6	Post
Oat Flakes	6	Post
Rice Bran	7	Ralston
Fruit Muesli	4	Ralston
Chex (multi Bran)	6	Ralston
Chex (wheat)	3	Ralston
Chex (oat)	5	Ralston
Chex (rice)	2	Ralston
Batman	10	Ralston
Double Chex	5	Ralston
Total Raisin Bran	14	General Mills
Total Whole Wheat	3	General Mills
Wheaties	3	General Mills
Total Corn Flakes	2	General Mills
Kix	3	General Mills
Fiber One	0	General Mills
Nutri Grain (almond raisin)	7	Kellogg's
Nutri Grain (wheat)	2	Kellogg's
Heartwise	9	Kellogg's
Kenmei Rice Bran	4	Kellogg's
Product 19	3	Kellogg's
Just Right	5	Kellogg's
Crispix	3	Kellogg's
All Bran	5	Kellogg's
Cracklin' Oat Bran	7	Kellogg's
Common Sense Oat Bran	10	Kellogg's
Oatbake (raisin nut)	8	Kellogg's
Oatbake (honey bran)	8	Kellogg's
Bran Flakes	5	Kellogg's
100% Natural Granola	7	Quaker
100% Granola (raisin and date)	8	Quaker

REAL MEANS

1.

In an American household, the TV is on for an average of 7 hours each day.

2.

The average life span of a hamster is 3 years.

3.

Children ages 10–13 get an average of 10 hours of sleep each night.

Z Z Z Z Z Z Z Z z z z

4.

Americans go to an average of 5 movies each year.

5.

Each American produces an average of 4 pounds of garbage a day.

From: Frank Kendid and Richard Hutton, *Life Spans, Or How Long Things Last* (New York: Holt, Rinehart & Winston, 1979); *The Book of Numbers*, compiled by the editors of Heron House Associates (New York: A & W Publishers, 1978); K. Long and T. Rein, *Kicking the Bucket* (New York: Quill, 1985).

Statistics: Middles, Means, and In-Betweens